Bethan James and Heather Stuart

READ AND PLAY

BIBLE

The Jesus Story

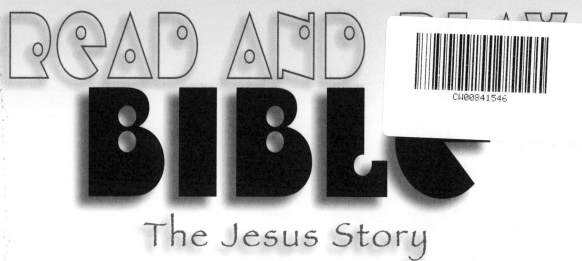

Read the story of Jesus,
his birth, life and teachings.
Then complete the puzzles and activities
to see how much you have discovered.

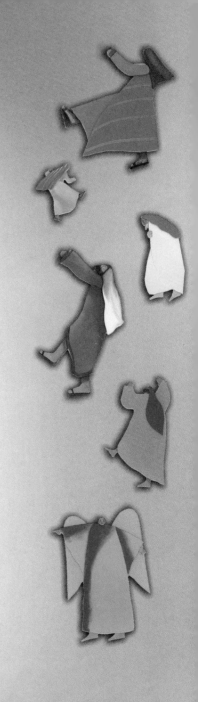

CONTENTS

A miracle in the temple 6
Mary and the angel 8
A visit to Elizabeth 10
Joseph dreams of angels 12
The Roman census 14
No room at the inn 16
A very starry night 18
Shepherds on the hillside 20
The baby in the manger 22
Simeon meets Jesus 24
A bright new star 26
The king in the palace 28
Wise men worship 30
A very bad dream 32
Escape to Egypt 34
Exiles in Egypt 36
A home in Nazareth 38
Lost and found 40
John the Baptist 42
Jesus is baptised 44
Jesus is tested 46
Jesus makes friends 48

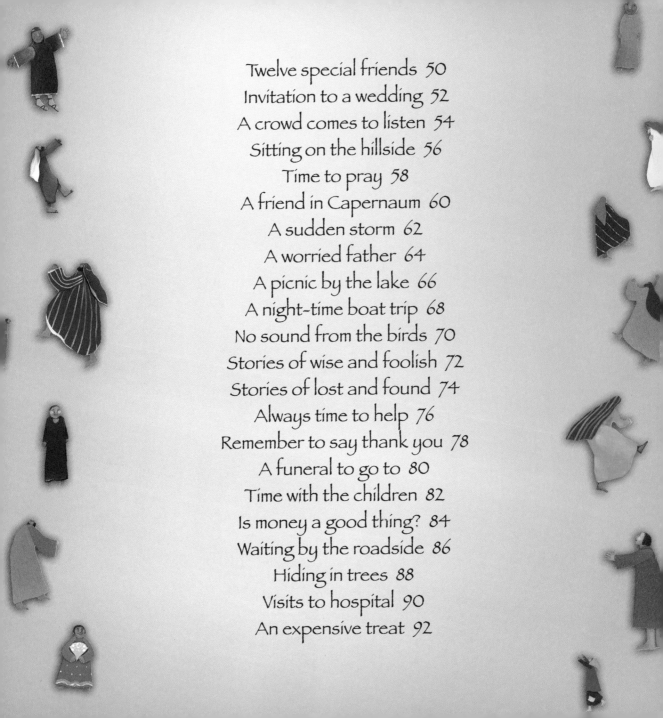

Twelve special friends 50
Invitation to a wedding 52
A crowd comes to listen 54
Sitting on the hillside 56
Time to pray 58
A friend in Capernaum 60
A sudden storm 62
A worried father 64
A picnic by the lake 66
A night-time boat trip 68
No sound from the birds 70
Stories of wise and foolish 72
Stories of lost and found 74
Always time to help 76
Remember to say thank you 78
A funeral to go to 80
Time with the children 82
Is money a good thing? 84
Waiting by the roadside 86
Hiding in trees 88
Visits to hospital 90
An expensive treat 92

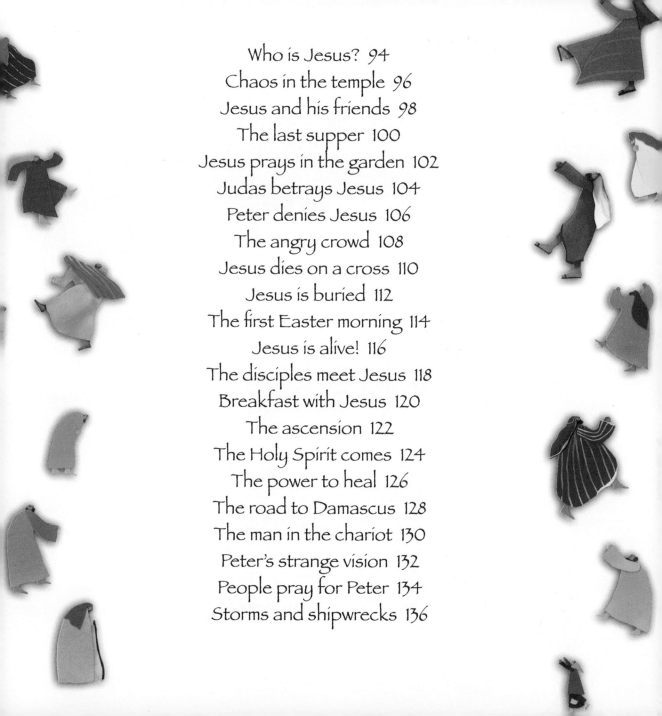

Who is Jesus? 94
Chaos in the temple 96
Jesus and his friends 98
The last supper 100
Jesus prays in the garden 102
Judas betrays Jesus 104
Peter denies Jesus 106
The angry crowd 108
Jesus dies on a cross 110
Jesus is buried 112
The first Easter morning 114
Jesus is alive! 116
The disciples meet Jesus 118
Breakfast with Jesus 120
The ascension 122
The Holy Spirit comes 124
The power to heal 126
The road to Damascus 128
The man in the chariot 130
Peter's strange vision 132
People pray for Peter 134
Storms and shipwrecks 136

A MIRACLE IN THE TEMPLE

In the great city of Jerusalem there was a temple.

One of the priests was called Zechariah. He and his wife Elizabeth had been praying for a long time because they wanted very much to have a baby.

One day, when Zechariah was burning incense in the temple, he saw an angel.

'God has answered your prayers,' the angel told him. 'Elizabeth will have a baby boy called John. When he grows up he will help get people ready for the time when Jesus is born.'

Zechariah was so shocked, he couldn't believe what the angel had said. He lost his voice and couldn't tell anyone what he had seen. But his wife Elizabeth soon found that she was expecting a baby…

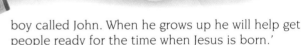

LOST AND FOUND

1 What did the priest lose?

2 What did the priest's wife gain?

HOW MANY NAMES?

How many names can you find in the grid?

E M P E T E R G
V N A A J O H N
E E U R M M T L
Z N L U K E H S

THE BABY'S NAME

What is the name of Elizabeth's baby?

MATCH THE TEMPLE

Which of these temple pictures exactly matches the temple picture on the opposite page?

A B

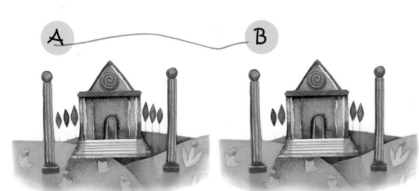

A B C

7

Mary and the Angel

Mary was a relative of Elizabeth's. She lived in a little village called Nazareth where it was hot and sunny.

One day, the same angel, the angel Gabriel, came to see Mary.

'Don't be afraid,' he said. 'I have a message for you from God. You are going to have a baby. His name will be Jesus, and he will be the Son of God.'

Mary opened her eyes wide with wonder. She loved God but she knew that you couldn't have a baby without a husband—and Mary wasn't married yet.

'Nothing is impossible for God, Mary,' the angel said. 'This special baby will be God's Son.'

PUZZLE

Write the number of the jigsaw piece in the box next to where it fits in the big picture.

C 5

1

D

A 9

E 4

B 10

F 20

8

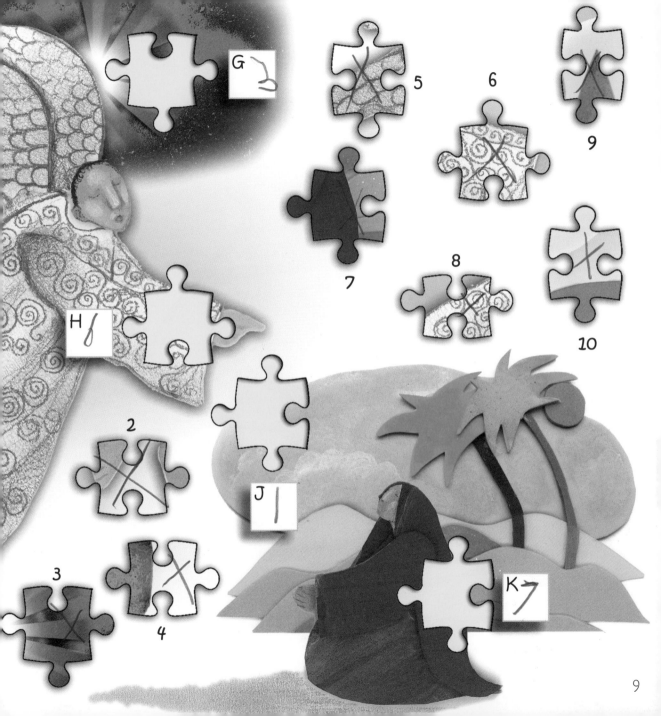

G

5

6

9

H

7

8

10

2

J

3

4

K

9

A VISIT TO ELIZABETH

Mary was very happy to know that God had chosen her to be the mother of his child. When she realised she was pregnant, she couldn't wait to tell someone the news. So she went to visit Elizabeth.

As soon as Elizabeth greeted Mary, the baby inside her jumped for joy! Then Elizabeth knew that something amazing had happened. She knew Mary's news before Mary told her.

'I'm so happy,' Mary sang to God. 'God has blessed me! God has chosen someone unimportant like me to do something great and wonderful for him!'

Mary stayed with Elizabeth for three months.

THE SHORT ROAD

Which is the shortest route to Elizabeth?

A

A
B
C

MAKE THE LINK

Draw a line from each man to connect him with the right object.

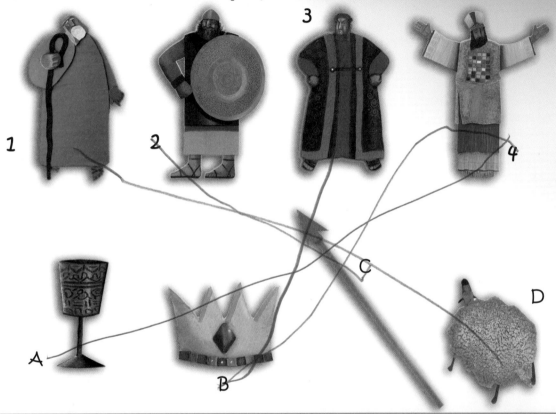

JOBS

What is the job of each of the men in the puzzle above? Write the answers in the boxes.

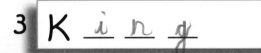

1 | S _ _ _ _ _ _ _ _

3 | K i n g

2 | S o l j e r _

4 | P _ _ _ _ _ _

JOSEPH DREAMS OF ANGELS

Mary's family had promised that one day she would be the wife of Joseph, the carpenter. Now that she was expecting a baby, Mary knew she had to tell Joseph about the angel and his message too. What would he think?

Joseph was a good, kind man. He was worried that people would say unkind things if Mary had a baby before they were married. How could he help her?

Then Joseph had a dream.

'It's OK, Joseph,' an angel said to him. 'This baby will be the person God has promised to send to save his people. Mary will need your help. Marry her and look after them both.'

So Joseph married Mary.

SHADOWS

Draw a line to connect each of these five dreamers with their shadows.

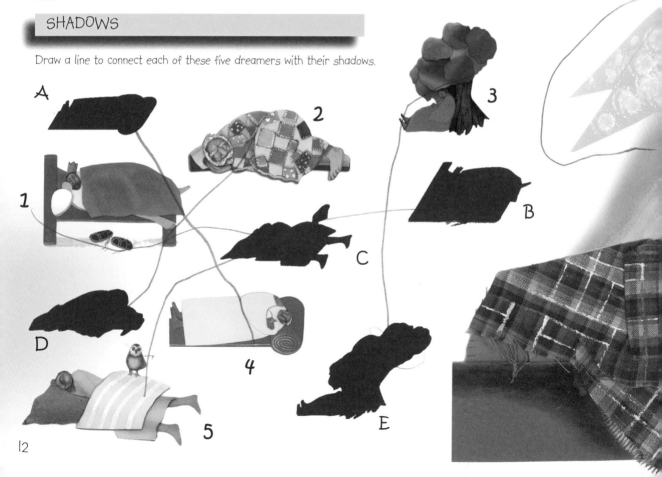

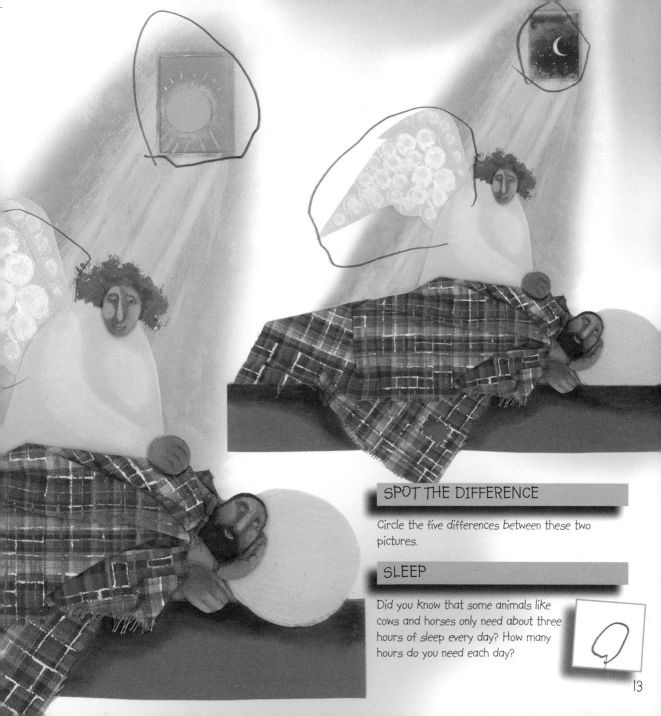

SPOT THE DIFFERENCE

Circle the five differences between these two pictures.

SLEEP

Did you know that some animals like cows and horses only need about three hours of sleep every day? How many hours do you need each day?

13

THE ROMAN CENSUS

The Roman emperor, Caesar Augustus, ruled over many lands. The place where Mary and Joseph lived was a very small part of his empire.

Now he wanted to count all his people. He didn't know that Mary's baby would be born soon. Even if he had known, he wouldn't have cared.

'Go to the place where your ancestors lived. I want to count you all so I know how much money I can collect in taxes!'

No one wanted to pay taxes to the Romans who lived in their country. But the people had no choice.

Mary didn't want to travel far from Nazareth. She wanted to have her baby in her own home. Joseph helped her to pack some things for the journey to Bethlehem, the home of Joseph's ancestor, King David, who had lived there many years before. They took some things for her baby just in case he was born there.

SPOT THE DIFFERENCE

Can you find all five differences between these two Roman soldiers?

14

MISSING LETTERS

What letter is missing from each of these words?
The same letter might be missing from a word more than once.

1 BTHLHM

2 EPEROR

3 JOSEH

4 MAY

5 ROANS

HOW MANY?

Look at the people at the top of the page and answer these questions.

a How many people are wearing green? 2

b How many people are wearing yellow? 0

c How many people are walking? 6

d How many animals are there? 2

No room at the inn

Mary and Joseph travelled along the road to Bethlehem with lots of other people.

When they arrived, the place was bustling with people looking for somewhere to stay. There were soldiers there getting ready for the census. The streets were full. The town was full. They had all come there to be counted.

There was no room for Mary and Joseph.

'You can rest in my stable,' said the innkeeper.

Mary was very tired. She was happy to have anywhere she could stop and rest. She didn't mind that there was straw on the floor. She didn't mind the smell of the animals.

SPOT THE DIFFERENCE

Find six differences between the two pictures.

TRUE OR FALSE?

Put a tick in the box if the statement is right; put a cross if it is wrong.

☐ 1 Mary and Joseph were the only people travelling.

☒ 2 There were Roman soldiers in Bethlehem.

☒ 3 It was very quiet in Bethlehem.

☐ 4 There was no room in the inn.

☐ 5 Mary refused to stay in the stable.

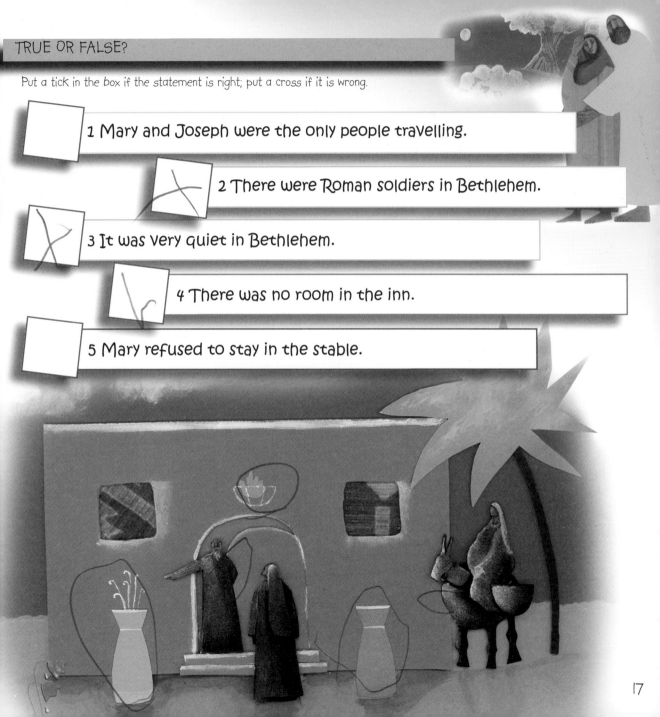

MATCH THE SHAPE

Which of these manger shapes is the same as in the big picture?

A   B   C

Which of these sleeping donkey shapes is the same as in the big picture?

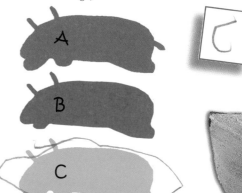

A

B

C

That night, when the cry of a tiny newborn baby was heard in the stable, the stars were shining brightly.

Mary called her little son Jesus, just as the angel had told her. She wrapped him up warmly in the strips of cloth she had brought with her, and made a bed for him in the manger.

He was just like any other baby who cried and fed and needed to be cuddled. But he was not like any other baby—because he was Jesus, God's own Son.

Mary stared at her baby, who, like the animals in the stable, was sleeping peacefully. She smiled at Joseph, amazed that this little miracle, Jesus, was here at last.

Find the answers to the questions inside the grid.

J M J O S E P H U
A A D A V I D M J
M T P J C R L A O
E T L J E S U S H
S M A N G E R H R

1 What was the name of Mary's son?

Jesus

2 What was the name of Mary's husband?

Joseph

19

SHEPHERDS ON THE HILLSIDE

That night, shepherds were out on the hills looking after their sheep. There were sounds of animals snuffling about and the fire crackling in the quiet. Then suddenly… there was bright light all around them!

'Don't be afraid,' said an angel. 'I have something wonderful to tell you! Jesus, God's own Son, has been born in Bethlehem. You'll know you have found him when you see him lying on a bed of hay.'

Then the sky was full of angels.

'Glory to God!' they sang. 'Peace to everyone who lives on earth.'

MAKE A CARD

1 Trace around the simple shapes of the angel.

2 Cut the shapes out from coloured card.

3 Stick the pieces on to your Christmas card.

4 You can draw on extra details.

Happy Christmas

5 Perhaps use some wool or string to give the angel hair.

6 Add your Christmas message at the top of the card.

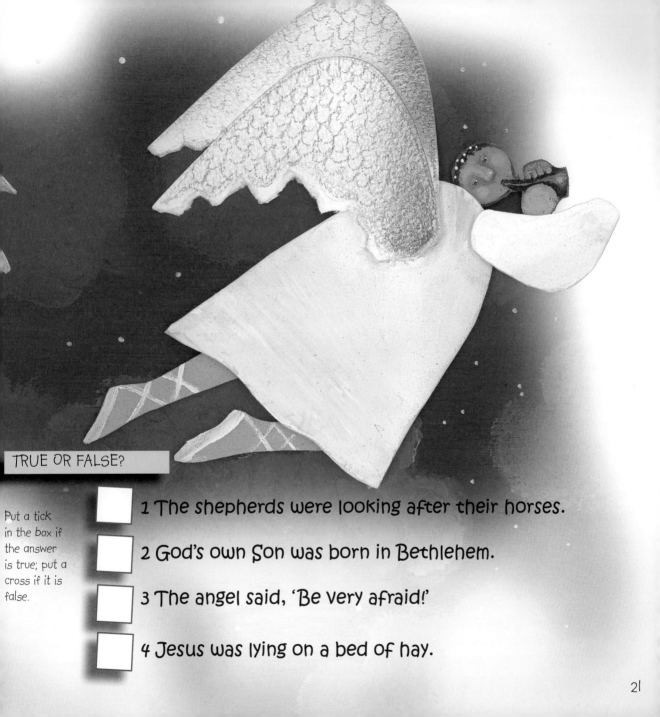

TRUE OR FALSE?

Put a tick in the box if the answer is true; put a cross if it is false.

☐ 1 The shepherds were looking after their horses.

☐ 2 God's own Son was born in Bethlehem.

☐ 3 The angel said, 'Be very afraid!'

☐ 4 Jesus was lying on a bed of hay.

21

THE BABY IN THE MANGER

The shepherds looked at one another and blinked hard. Did they really see what they thought they had seen? Did they really hear what they thought they had heard?

They had to find out. They ran to Bethlehem and there they saw the baby in the manger. Here he was, the Son of God, and here was his mother Mary.

Who heard about it first? Who saw the baby Jesus before anyone else? They did—poor shepherds. They were amazed.

They told Mary and Joseph about the angels and what they had said. Then they went back to their sheep, praising God because his own Son had been born—and they had seen him!

Use the code to write down three messages opposite.

+ = a   *=e   ^=i   #=o $=u

Th* sh*ph*rds r+n t# B*thl*h*m.

1

Th*y f#$nd th* b+by
ly^ng ^n + m+ng*r.

2

Th*y pr+^s*d G#d b*c+$s*
J*s$s h+d b**n b#rn.

3

SIMEON MEETS JESUS

It was the custom to have a thanksgiving service when a baby was a few weeks' old. So Mary and Joseph took Jesus to the temple to thank God for his birth. Joseph had brought two doves as a thank you offering.

When they went into the temple courtyard, a man called Simeon came up to them. Simeon had been waiting a very long time for the Saviour God had promised. Now he had seen him.

'Now I can die in peace,' Simeon prayed, 'because I have seen Jesus, the child who will save his people and show everyone how great you are.'

CONNECTIONS

Draw a line connecting each yellow box with the correct pink box.

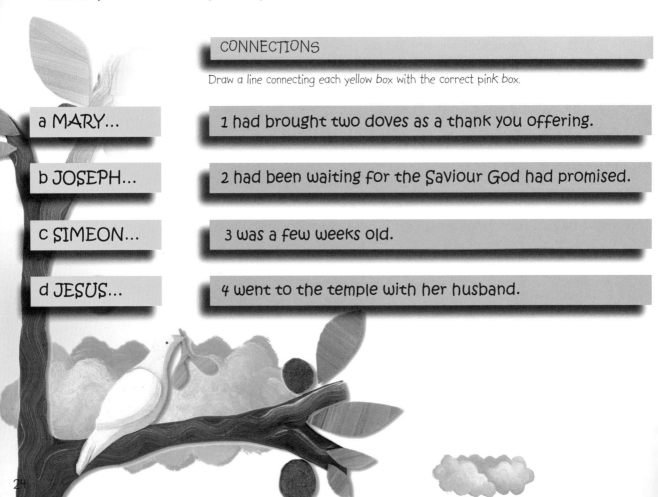

a MARY...

b JOSEPH...

c SIMEON...

d JESUS...

1 had brought two doves as a thank you offering.

2 had been waiting for the Saviour God had promised.

3 was a few weeks old.

4 went to the temple with her husband.

1 Now I can die in

....

2 because I have seen

....

3 the child who will

....

his people and show everyone
how great God is.

MISSING WORDS

What did Simeon say?
Fill in the missing words.

A BRIGHT NEW STAR

The night sky was bright with many stars. Tonight there was a new star.

Wise men far away in the east were studying the sky. They looked at their charts. They talked with each other. They wondered what it could mean.

'A new king has been born,' they decided.

'A king for the Jewish people,' they thought.

'We must go to worship and welcome him,' they agreed.

They packed treasure chests and took special gifts and travelled west on their camels, following the star.

QUIZ

1 Where did the wise men come from?

2 How did they travel?

3 What did they see in the sky?

4 Who did they think had been born?

Find four differences between the two pictures.

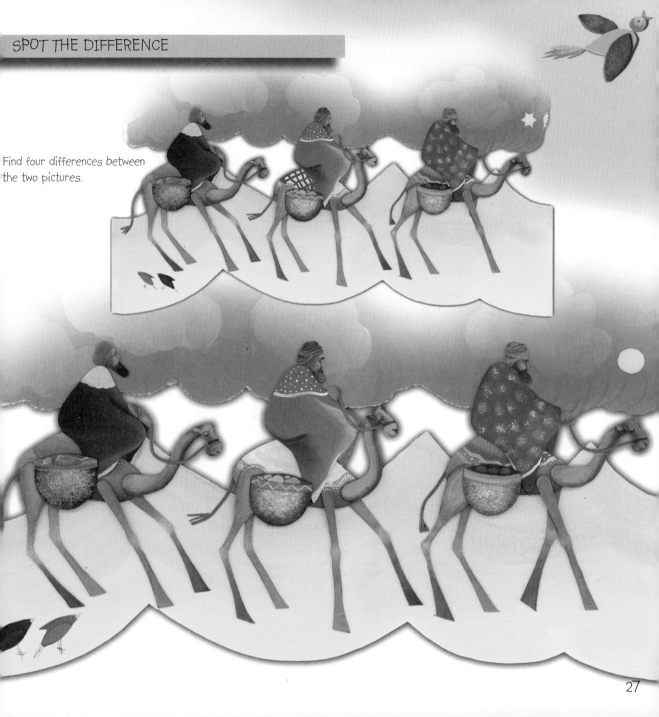

THE KING IN THE PALACE

After some time they arrived in Jerusalem. They thought a king would be born in a palace, so they went to see King Herod.

'A king?' said King Herod. 'I am the only king here. Tell me more about this baby king...'

The wise men explained about the new star and what they thought it meant. King Herod looked from one to the other. He thought very hard. Then he talked to his advisers, who studied their scrolls.

'Bethlehem,' the advisers said nervously. 'The new baby king promised by God would be born in... Bethlehem.'

'Make sure you come back this way,' Herod called after the wise men. 'Then I can go and worship him too...'

THE KING'S THINGS

Can you untangle these letters to find three things that belong to the king?

1 TORHNE

2 ACELAP

3 WNORC

A   B   C   D

WHICH WAY?

Which way leads to Bethlehem?

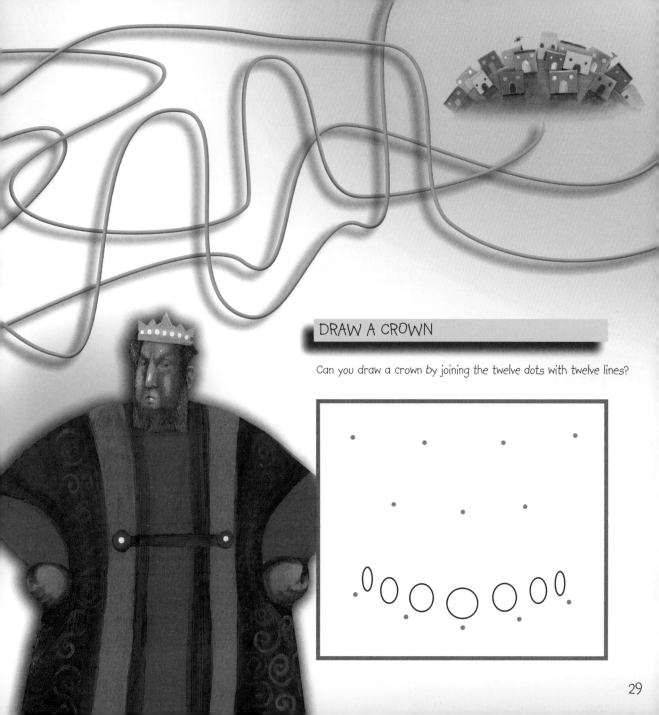

DRAW A CROWN

Can you draw a crown by joining the twelve dots with twelve lines?

WISE MEN WORSHIP

The wise men from the east left the palace and followed the star south towards Bethlehem.

They did not feel happy about their visit to King Herod. They were not sure they could trust him. Soon they reached Bethlehem and travelled along the long road through the town. They thought the star seemed to stop above a little house there, and they got down from their camels to see.

Mary was inside the house with her little son. They greeted her and brought inside their gifts. They offered them to her: gold, frankincense and myrrh. Then they knelt and worshipped Jesus, the newborn king of the Jewish people.

The wise men came from the east travelling first west then south.
If north is at the top, can you show which way is east, west and south?
Write your answers in the boxes below.

NORTH

1

2

3

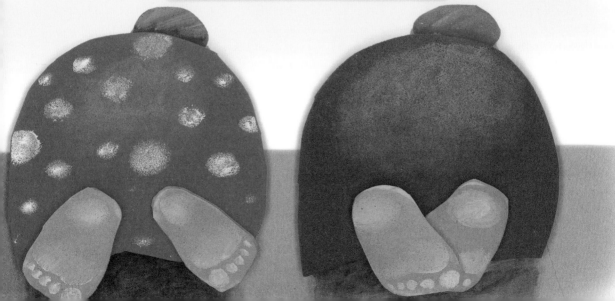

A VERY BAD DREAM

The road to Jerusalem was their way home again to their lands in the east. The wise men rested before returning. As they slept, they dreamed.

They dreamed that they should go back home another way. They dreamed that they should not go back to tell King Herod that they had found the baby king. They dreamed that King Herod wanted to harm him.

They mounted their camels and made their way eastwards without going through Jerusalem.

King Herod paced up and down, waiting for their visit. When they did not return, he was very angry.

1 Who was looking after their sheep?

2 The wise men came from the _____.

3 Which King lived in Jerusalem?

4 Mary travelled with _____.

5 Mary put Jesus in a _____.

QUESTIONS AND ANSWERS

Each yellow box contains a question.
All the answers are in the blue boxes.
Write the correct question number next to each answer.

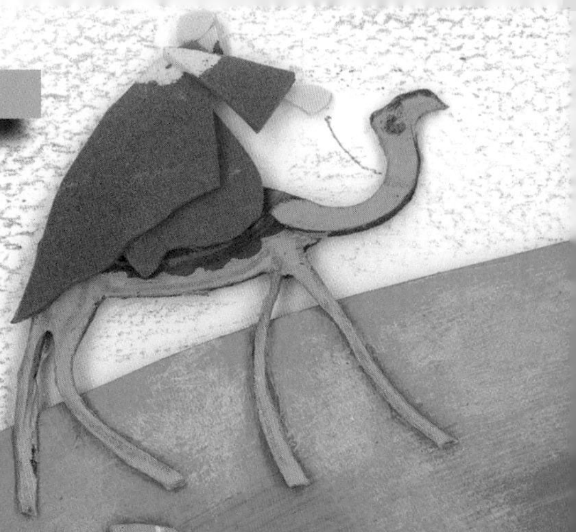

6 Mary had a _____ .

7 The Roman emperor ordered a _____ .

8 The sky was full of _____ .

9 The wise men followed a _____ .

HEROD

ANGELS

BABY

JOSEPH

EAST

MANGER

SHEPHERDS

CENSUS

STAR

33

ESCAPE TO EGYPT

The wise men were not the only people to dream about King Herod.

That night Joseph was also troubled by dreams. He dreamed that an angel warned him to take his family away to Egypt. King Herod would not rest until he had found the baby king and destroyed him. King Herod wanted to be the only king in the land.

Joseph woke Mary and together they gathered all they needed for their journey. They escaped to Egypt by night, taking Mary's little son to safety.

WHO DREAMED WHAT?

Draw a line connecting each green box with the correct pink box.

a Elizabeth dreamed she

b Joseph dreamed he

c Simeon dreamed he

d The wise men dreamed they

1 should go home another way.

2 would have a baby one day.

3 should marry Mary.

4 would one day see Jesus.

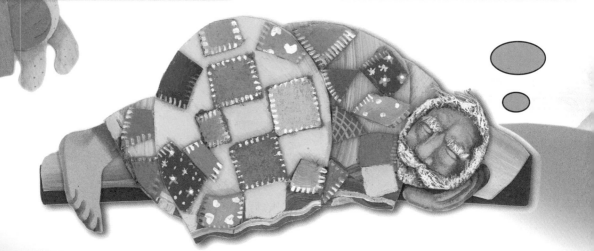

34

WHAT'S MISSING?

Compare these similar pictures. There are six things missing on the smaller picture that appear on the larger one. Find them and draw a circle around them.

EXILES IN EGYPT

Mary and Joseph lived for a while in Egypt. They made it their home as some of their ancestors had many, many years before.

They remembered that Abraham and Sarah had lived there when there was a famine in Canaan. They remembered that Jacob's favourite son, Joseph, had been taken there as a slave. They remembered that Moses had led God's people out of Egypt and that they celebrated their freedom from slavery at the Passover Feast each year.

Some time later, Joseph dreamed again. This time the angel told him that it was safe to return to the land of Israel because King Herod had died.

WHERE DID THEY GO?

Which is the right answer, a, b or c?

1 Abraham and Sarah went to Egypt

B
A on holiday
B to escape a famine
C to see the pyramids

2 Joseph went to Egypt

A as a tourist
B to look for a new job
C as a slave

3 Moses went to Egypt

A to look for food
B to lead God's people out of slavery
C to escape from the plagues

CAPTION THE PICTURES

Complete the captions by filling in the missing names.

1 ....
had led God's people out of Egypt

2 ....
was told by an angel that he could leave Egypt

3 ....
Jacob's favourite son, rose to power in Egypt

4 ....
lived in Egypt when there was a famine

A HOME IN NAZARETH

Mary, Joseph and Jesus left Egypt and travelled north again. But when they heard that Herod's son was now in charge in Jerusalem, they decided to travel further north. They settled in the small village of Nazareth in Galilee, far enough from Jerusalem to live quietly.

Jesus grew up in Nazareth like all the other boys. He watched Joseph work as a carpenter there and he learned how to handle tools as he did. Jesus learned how to be a carpenter as Joseph was.

Mary watched her son grow up and for a while she forgot the strange visitors who had come to see them while they were in Bethlehem.

START

WHICH WAY?

Draw a line through the maze to show the right route for Joseph, Mary and Jesus to follow.

39

LOST AND FOUND

When Jesus was twelve, Mary and Joseph travelled with everyone else to Jerusalem for the Passover Festival as they did every year. They looked forward to the celebrations. They enjoyed the holiday away from their quiet village.

On the way back, Mary asked Joseph where Jesus was. Joseph had thought he was with the other boys. They began to look for him among their friends and family. But no one had seen Jesus.

Mary and Joseph left the group and hurried back to Jerusalem. They looked for three days before they found him in the temple.

'Is this your son?' the teachers asked Mary. 'You have taught him well. He knows more than we do!'

Mary was very pleased to see him safe. She had been very worried.

'I had to be in my Father's house,' he told them.

FIND JESUS

START

Can you help Mary and Joseph to find Jesus in the temple?

Congratulations! You have
found Jesus in the temple.

41

JOHN THE BAPTIST

While Jesus was growing up, Elizabeth's son, John, was growing up too.

When he was a man, he spent time in the desert, praying and getting ready for the work God had planned for him.

Then he started teaching the people about the way God wanted them to live.

'It's time to be sorry for the bad things you have done,' he told them. 'It's time to get ready. Someone very special is coming.'

John didn't dress like other people and he ate simple foods like locusts and honey. He looked wild and strange. But people came to listen to him. They told God they were sorry and John baptised them in the River Jordan.

WHAT DID HE SAY?

What did John tell the people? Put a tick or a cross in each box to show whether the statements are true.

1 'Get ready! Someone very special is coming.'

2 'It's time to be sorry for the bad things you have done.'

3 'Eat locusts and honey. They are good for you.'

4 'Where can I get a good hair cut?'

WHAT IS THIS FOOD?

Unscramble the letters to find the answer.

YENHO

43

JESUS IS BAPTISED

Jesus watched from the bank as John baptised people. Then he stepped forward.

'I want you to baptise me, John,' he said.

John knew that God had sent Jesus. He knew that the work he was going to do was very special.

'I can't baptise you—you have done nothing wrong. Unlike the rest of us, you have nothing to be sorry for. You should baptise me instead!'

'This is what God wants,' said Jesus.

John went with Jesus into the water and Jesus was baptised.

Then everyone heard a voice from heaven.

'This is my very own Son and I love him. Everything he does is good and makes me happy.'

COMPLETE THE SENTENCE

Draw a line connecting each pink box with the correct yellow box.

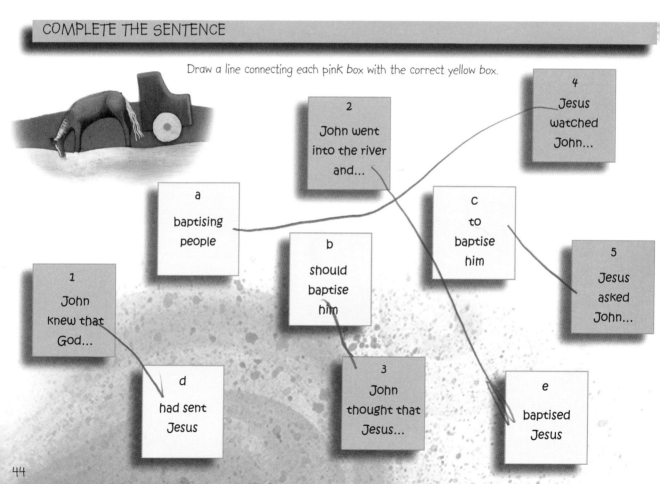

2
John went into the river and...

4
Jesus watched John...

a
baptising people

c
to baptise him

5
Jesus asked John...

b
should baptise him

1
John knew that God...

d
had sent Jesus

3
John thought that Jesus...

e
baptised Jesus

TRUE OR FALSE?

Tick the right answers and put a cross beside the wrong answers.

1 People were baptised with water.

2 People were baptised to show God they were sorry.

3 People were baptised only on Sundays.

COPY THE PICTURE

Can you copy the picture into the box opposite? Use the grid of black squares to help you.

JESUS IS TESTED

Then Jesus went into the desert. He had nothing to eat for 40 days and 40 nights.

'If you're hungry,' said a voice beside him, 'you could always make these stones into bread.'

'No!' said Jesus. 'The scriptures tell us there is more to life than food. We need to listen to God too.'

The voice was the voice of the devil. He took Jesus to the top of the temple.

'If you're really God's Son, you could jump,' he said. 'God will send angels to keep you safe.'

'No. The scriptures also say you must not test God like this.'

The devil then took Jesus to the top of a mountain.

'Worship me and I will give you all that you can see,' said the devil.

'No!' said Jesus. 'The scriptures say we must worship God and no one else.'

FILL IN THE MISSING WORDS

1 'If you're hungry,' said a voice beside him, 'you could make these stones into...

,

___ ___ ___ ___ ___

WHO IS THIS?

1 Who was tempted by Satan to eat forbidden fruit?

2 What was the name of her husband?

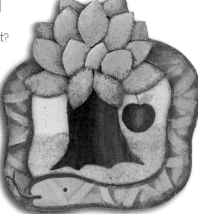

46

2 'If you're really God's...

___ ___ ___

you could jump,' he said.
'God will send angels
to keep you safe.'

3 'Worship...

___ ___

and I will give you all
that you can...
,

___ ___ ___

JESUS MAKES FRIENDS

Jesus had moved with his mother from Nazareth in the hills to Capernaum beside the waters of Lake Galilee.

The fishermen who worked on the boats knew him. The tax collectors knew him. Everyone listened when Jesus spoke to them.

Jesus told the two brothers, Peter and Andrew, to put out their fishing nets on the other side of the boat—and their nets nearly broke with the weight of the fish they caught. Their friends, James and John, who were also brothers, came to help.

'Leave your nets,' said Jesus. 'Come with me.'

WHAT HAPPENED NEXT?

Put a tick in the box next to the correct answer.

1 The fishermen went home to have their lunch. ☐

2 The fishermen left their nets and followed Jesus. ☐

3 The fishermen got back in their boats and went fishing. ☐

PUZZLE PIECES

Four puzzle pieces fit in picture A and four fit in picture B. Write 'A' or 'B' in the boxes below.

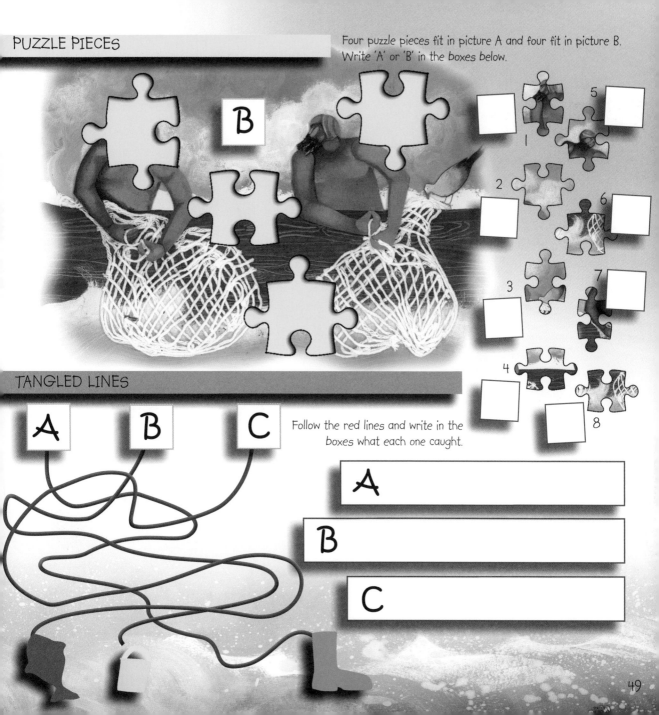

B

1

5

2

6

3

7

4

8

TANGLED LINES

A   B   C

Follow the red lines and write in the boxes what each one caught.

A

B

C

Twelve special friends

TRUE OR FALSE?

What do you know about the disciples?
Put a tick or a cross beside each statement.

☐ 1 Peter and John were brothers.

☐ 2 Philip was from Rome.

☐ 3 Thomas was a twin.

☐ 4 There were ten disciples altogether.

ODD ONE OUT

Draw a line between the man's name and the job he did.

Peter

Matthew

James

Philip

John

Andrew

Fisherman

Tax collector

So the odd one out is:

Jesus knew the tax collectors who lived in Capernaum. Sometimes they listened when he talked about God and how much he loved them.

'Come with me,' Jesus said to Matthew. And Matthew got up and followed Jesus.

Peter and Andrew were brothers from Bethsaida. James and John were brothers too, sons of Zebedee. Philip, a fisherman from Bethsaida, followed Jesus, and Bartholomew, Thomas the twin, Matthew, James, Simon, Thaddaeus and Judas Iscariot also became his friends.

The twelve men were known as disciples of Jesus.

Their lives changed completely once they had decided to follow Jesus.

50

PUZZLE PIECES

Number the puzzle pieces to show where they go to complete the picture.

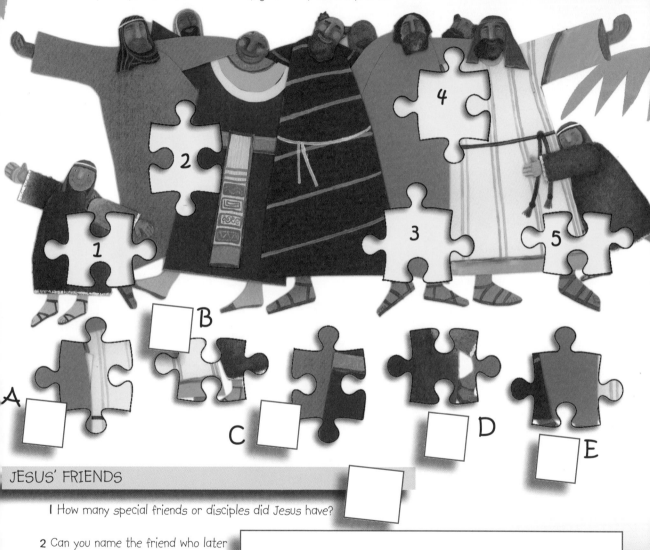

JESUS' FRIENDS

1 How many special friends or disciples did Jesus have?

2 Can you name the friend who later became an enemy of Jesus?

INVITATION TO A WEDDING

Mary had been invited to a wedding in the little village of Cana. Jesus and his friends went too. The whole village seemed to be there celebrating!

Everyone was very happy for the bride and groom. After a while Mary noticed that there was no more wine left.

'Can you help?' Mary whispered to Jesus. Jesus went quietly to talk with the servants. He asked them to fill six huge jars full of water. Then he asked them to take a cup of water drawn from the jars to the man in charge of the feast.

'What wonderful wine!' he said as he tasted it.

Mary knew and the servant knew—and the disciples knew—that Jesus had made the water into the very best wine. It was a miracle.

A B C D E

WEDDING GUESTS

Match the silhouettes to the six guests in the picture above and write the correct letter in the boxes.

1 2 3 4

WHAT HAPPENED WHERE?

Complete the sentences by drawing a line connecting each blue spot to the correct red spot.

1 Jesus changed water into wine in   ●   ● **a** Galilee

2 Jesus asked Matthew to be his friend in   ●   ● **b** Nazareth

3 Jesus was born in   ●   ● **c** Bethsaida

4 Jesus lived by Lake   ●   ● **d** Cana

5 Peter, Andrew and Philip came from   ●   ● **e** Bethlehem

6 Jesus came from   ●   ● **f** Capernaum

F

G

H

I

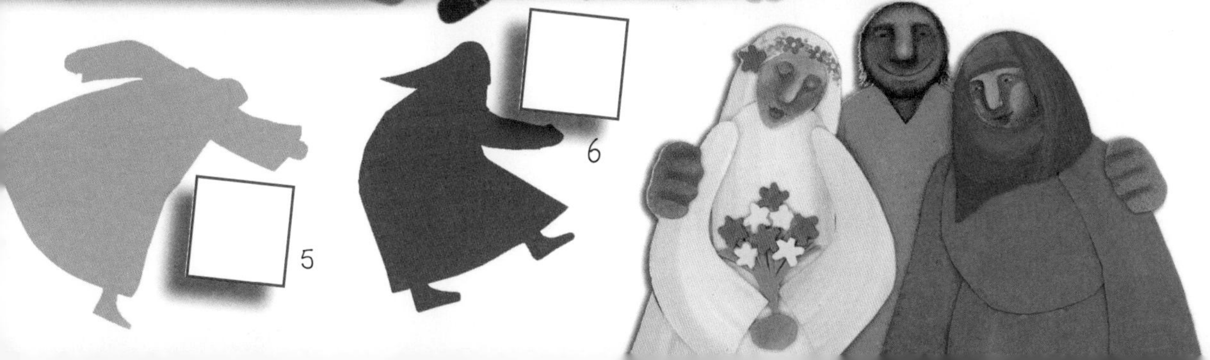

5

6

A CROWD COMES TO LISTEN

Before long people in Capernaum came to find out all that Jesus knew about God. They wanted to ask him questions.

When people heard that Jesus had healed Peter's mother-in-law of a fever, they also wanted him to heal other people they knew.

Four friends came to Jesus for help. They were carrying a man on a mat but saw there was no

room to get into the house. Thinking quickly, they carried him up to the roof and began to make a hole in it.

Soon they had lowered their friend down in front of Jesus. Everyone in the room looked at the mess they had made. But Jesus saw the man who couldn't walk; he saw that his friends cared about him and believed that Jesus could help him.

'Pick up your bed and walk,' said Jesus.

The man was healed! He walked home that night a happy man.

WORDSEARCH

Use these clues below to find the answers in the box:

1 Whose mother-in-law had Jesus healed?

2 How many friends helped the paralysed man?

3 Where did they make a hole?

4 What could their friend not do?

A	O	F	A	T	E	L	E	E	N	H	L	A	E	C
S	M	O	M	R	T	A	A	E	R	E	D	S	L	I
G	F	O	U	R	C	Z	A	R	W	H	Z	D	E	O
O	T	E	R	E	M	A	Y	T	A	B	E	U	R	D
L	H	U	Y	Y	I	R	L	N	L	E	D	L	O	Z
D	A	L	P	E	T	E	R	N	K	R	P	O	O	S
L	T	M	N	R	H	S	I	P	S	O	F	S	F	R

FIND THE MATCH

Which little picture is exactly the same as the big picture?

A

B

C

55

SITTING ON THE HILLSIDE

Jesus taught people how to live so that they would be happy and God would be happy too.

'God will bless you if you need his help. He will comfort you if you are sad. If you long for good things, God will give you what you need. God will be kind to you if you are kind to other people.

'Forgive people who hurt you. Love your enemies and pray for them.

'Don't worry so much about things that don't matter. God feeds the birds and makes the flowers beautiful. He will take care of you too! Trust God and everything else will fall into place. God will make sure you have all you need.'

JESUS SAID

Complete these quotes. Jesus said...

2 Love your ....

1 Don't ....

COMPLETE THE SENTENCES

Draw a line connecting each pink box with the correct blue box.

1 God will bless you	a and pray for them.
2 God will comfort you	b who hurt you.
3 God will be kind to you	c if you need his help.
4 Forgive people	d if you are sad.
5 Love your enemies	e if you are kind to others.

MORE THINGS JESUS SAID

Trust . . . .
and everything else will fall
into place.

Fill in the missing words.

Forgive people who

. . . .

57

TIME TO PRAY

'Teach us to pray,' people said to Jesus.

'OK,' Jesus answered. 'The secret is to spend time alone with God as if you are talking to a father who cares about you and wants the best for you. You don't have to use long words or pretend to be what you are not. Be honest and tell God what's worrying you; tell him what you need. God is there. He will listen and he will answer you (but remember the answer may not always be what you expect!).

'Ask God to forgive you when you do things you know are wrong—but make sure you forgive other people who have hurt you first!' Jesus taught his disciples a pattern for praying to God.

It has been used by Christians for centuries. Can you pray it?

The Lord's Prayer

Our Father in heaven,

hallowed be your name,

your kingdom come,

your will be done,

on earth as in heaven.

Give us today our daily bread,

forgive us our sins

as we forgive

those who sin against us.

Lead us not into temptation

but deliver us from evil.

For the kingdom, the power,

and the glory are yours

now and for ever. Amen

PRAYERS

What will you pray for? Write down in the boxes below:

Something you want to thank God for

Something you want to ask God for

Something you need God to help you with

Someone else who needs God's help

Fill in the missing words. Can you do this from memory?

Our Father in heaven,
hallowed be your ...

> 1

your Kingdom come,
your will be ...
on earth as in heaven.

> 2

Give us today our daily ...

> 3

forgive us our sins
as we ...
those who sin against us.

> 4

Lead us not into ...
but deliver us from evil.

> 5

For the Kingdom, the ...
and the glory are yours

> 6

now and for ever. ...

> 7

A friend in Capernaum

There was a Roman soldier in Capernaum who was, unlike most Roman soldiers, popular with the people who lived there. He had even built them a synagogue.

The soldier knew all about Jesus. So when his servant became very ill, he came to ask Jesus for help.

'I will come immediately,' Jesus said.

But the Roman soldier wouldn't let him.

'You are far too great to come into my home!' he replied. 'No, just say the word and I know you have the power to heal him.'

Jesus had never met anyone who trusted him in this way.

'You can go home now,' Jesus told him. 'You will find that your servant is well.'

And he was.

SPOT THE DIFFERENCE

Can you find six differences between the pictures above and below?

Choose the correct puzzle piece for each space in the picture and put a tick next to it.

A SUDDEN STORM

Jesus was very tired. He spent a lot of his time helping other people and healing them. As soon as he got into the boat to cross to the other side of the lake, he put his head on a cushion and fell asleep.

The waters of Lake Galilee had been calm before but a sudden storm blew up. The wind whipped up choppy waves. The disciples had to bail out the water that was filling the boat. Soon even the fishermen were afraid.

'Jesus, wake up!' shouted his friends.

'Jesus, we need you!' they shouted again.

Jesus woke up. He stood up and spoke to the wind and the waves.

'Be calm! Be still!' he said.

Then, just as suddenly as it had started, everything was calm again.

The disciples looked at each other, amazed. Even the wind and waves listened when Jesus spoke.

WHAT HAPPENED NEXT?

What happened when the disciples asked Jesus for help? Tick the correct box.

☐ 1 Jesus told the disciples he wanted to go back to sleep.

☐ 2 Jesus helped bail water out of the boat.

☐ 3 Jesus said he didn't know anything about sailing.

☐ 4 Jesus calmed the storm.

HOW MANY FISH?

Put a tick if the statement is correct and a cross if it is wrong.

1 There are more than 40 fish in the boat.

2 There are only three yellow fish in the boat.

3 There are more green fish than blue fish in the boat.

4 The biggest fish is green.

WHO'S IN THE BOAT?

Put a tick next to the three men that are in the boat with Jesus.

1

2

3

4

5

6

A WORRIED FATHER

someone had needed his help and he knew that person had now been healed. Jesus looked around.

'I'm sorry,' said a woman beside him. 'I've been ill for so long. I knew if I just touched your cloak, it would be enough.'

Jairus was pushing his way through the crowd of people around Jesus.

'Please, come quickly!' he said. 'My little girl is dying!'

Jesus was anxious to help. But as he made his way through the people to reach Jairus' house, he stopped suddenly. Someone had touched him;

Jesus smiled at the woman, but as he turned to go to Jairus' house, a man came to say it was too late. Jairus' daughter had died. Jairus looked horrified.

'Trust me,' said Jesus.

Everyone at the house was crying. But Jesus held the little girl's hand.

'Wake up,' he said softly. And Jairus' daughter opened her eyes and sat up.

MAZE

Find your way through the
crowd to the home of Jairus.

START

FINISH

A PICNIC BY THE LAKE

Jesus had been teaching a huge crowd of people in a town near Lake Galilee. He had healed many people who were ill. Now it was late.

'We must find something for these people to eat,' Jesus told his twelve friends. 'They must be hungry and they are far from home.'

Philip was worried. He could see there were over 5000 people there!

'This boy has five pieces of bread and two fish,' said Andrew. 'But it won't go very far!'

Jesus thanked God for the bread and the fish and broke them up for his friends to share with all the people.

Each person shared with someone else. Everyone had something to eat and no one was hungry. There were even twelve baskets full of the leftovers. It was a miracle!

MATCH THE BASKETS

Number the baskets to match the baskets on page 67.

HOW MANY?

1 How many baskets contain bread?

2 How many baskets have no bread inside?

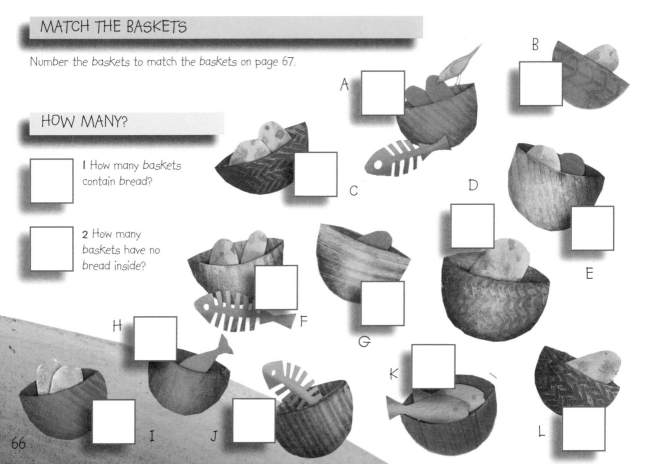

66

NUMBER QUIZ

1 How many friends of Jesus?

2 How many pieces of bread?

3 How many fish?

4 How many baskets of leftovers?

5 Add all the numbers together.

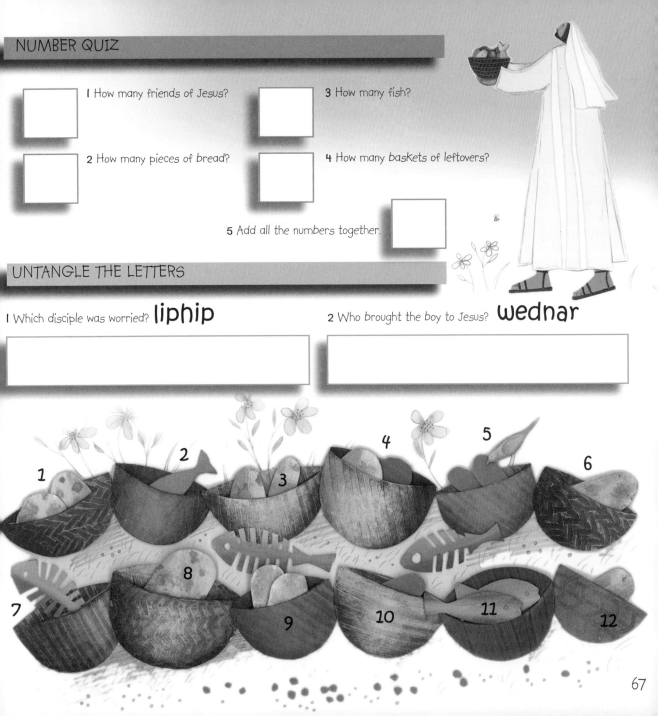

UNTANGLE THE LETTERS

1 Which disciple was worried? **liphip**

2 Who brought the boy to Jesus? **wednar**

67

A NIGHT~TIME BOAT TRIP

That evening, Jesus told his friends to take the boat across Lake Galilee while he stayed to pray for a while.

They were still sailing when they saw a figure approach them, walking on the water. At first they were frightened!

'Don't be afraid!' Jesus called out to them. 'It's only me.'

'Let me come to you on the water,' Peter replied, climbing out of the boat. At first he walked on the water too, but then the wind blew hard and Peter looked at the waves—and he began to sink.

'Help me!' Peter called out.

Jesus caught his hand and helped him into the boat.

The disciples had stared in wonder at all that had happened.

'You really are God's Son!' they said.

SPOT THE DIFFERENCE

Can you spot five differences between these two pictures?

68

```
A O T L Y E L A E N P E E Z S
S M F E P Y M I J E E W R E D
G F O G A L I L E E T S R D U
O T N M T E P R S H E L P P L
E V E N I N G U U S R E L F O
D A U R A T L I S U A T D A S
```

Find the answers to the questions in the wordsearch.

1 What was the name of the lake?

2 Who walked on the water?

3 Who went under the water?

4 What time of day was it?

5 What did Peter call out?

69

No Sound from the Birds

There were many birds flying over Lake Galilee. Sometimes they made lots of noise. One day Jesus met a man who couldn't hear the sound of the birds at all. He couldn't hear anything. He couldn't speak either.

'Can you help him?' his friends asked Jesus.

Jesus took him away from the other people gathered round. Then he touched the man's ears and tongue, and prayed.

Then the man was healed. Suddenly he could hear the birds cawing and screeching, and he began to speak for the first time.

Jesus took the man back to his friends. They were so happy, they couldn't stop talking about what Jesus had done.

SPOT THE BIRDS

Fill in the gaps to identify three birds.

1 _r_ _ _b_ _ _n_

2 _e_ _ _g_ _ _e_

3 _p_ _ _r_ _r_ _ _t_

NOISES

Oink!

Draw the animals that make these noises.

1

Moo!

2

70

MIRACLES

Complete the sentences about some of the miracles Jesus performed.

1 Jesus turned water into

2 Jesus healed a paralysed man so he could

3 Jesus healed a soldier's

4 Jesus calmed a

5 Jesus fed over 5000 people with bread and two little

6 Jesus walked on

WATER TO WINE

Colour in the picture to change the water into wine.

STORIES OF WISE AND FOOLISH

People often asked Jesus questions. Sometimes he would answer them by telling them a story.

'Don't just listen to the things I tell you. If you are wise, you will act on them and use them to guide you. Be like the wise man who built his house on solid rock. It took a long time and it was hard work—but when the storm came, he was warm and safe inside.

'Don't be like the foolish man! He didn't like hard work. He built on the sand where it was easy to dig. It didn't take him long to build—but as soon as the storm came, his house crumbled around him and was blown away.

'Listen to what is good and right and true and don't take shortcuts. In the end you will be safe and happy.'

MISTAKES

There are five mistakes in this extract from the story above. Circle the five incorrect words.

Be like the wise man who built his house on seaside rock. It took a long time and it was hard work—but when the elephant came, he was warm and safe inside.

'Don't be like the foolish man! He didn't like unpaid work. He built on the jelly where it was easy to dig. It didn't take him long to build—but as soon as the storm came, his mouse crumbled around him and was blown away.

TRUE OR FALSE?

Only some of the things below were taught by Jesus.
Tick the things he taught us.

1 God wants us to tell lies.

2 God is like a very good father.

3 God wants us to forgive people who treat us badly.

4 God does not have time to listen to our prayers.

5 God wants us to share what we have.

6 God loves the people he has made.

7 God wants us to fight and hurt each other.

8 God wants us to be kind to other people.

73

STORIES OF LOST AND FOUND

Jesus taught people that God loved them. He wanted them to be his friends; he wanted them to be happy.

'If you owned 100 sheep and found that just one had wandered off and got lost, what would you do?' said Jesus. 'You would search everywhere, high and low, until you found that little lost sheep and brought it home again. Then you would celebrate!

'God is just like that. He cares if only one person is lost and lonely or has chosen to wander away from him. He will only be happy when everyone is safe home again. 'God is like a loving father whose son has chosen to leave his family and go off by himself.

START

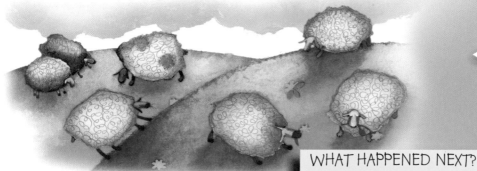

'The father watches and waits until his son has spent all his money and lost all his friends; he waits until his son is unhappy and lonely and realises he has made a mistake. He waits until his son realises that if he says sorry, he might be able to come home.

'Then the boy sees that his father is waiting for him. Before he can tell him how sorry he is, his father is hugging him and making plans for a party to welcome him home!

'God waits for us to know how much we need him and then he welcomes us back as part of his family.'

WHAT HAPPENED NEXT?

What does the loving father do?
Tick the right answers and put a cross next to the wrong ones.

1 The father refuses to speak to his son when he comes home. ☐

3 The father tells his son he can sleep in the barn. ☐

2 The father tells his son there is no room for him at home any more. ☐

4 The father throws a party. ☐

FIND THE LOST SHEEP

Can you find the path to the sheep, and then take the sheep home?

5 The father tells him he can work for his food.

FINISH

ALWAYS TIME TO HELP

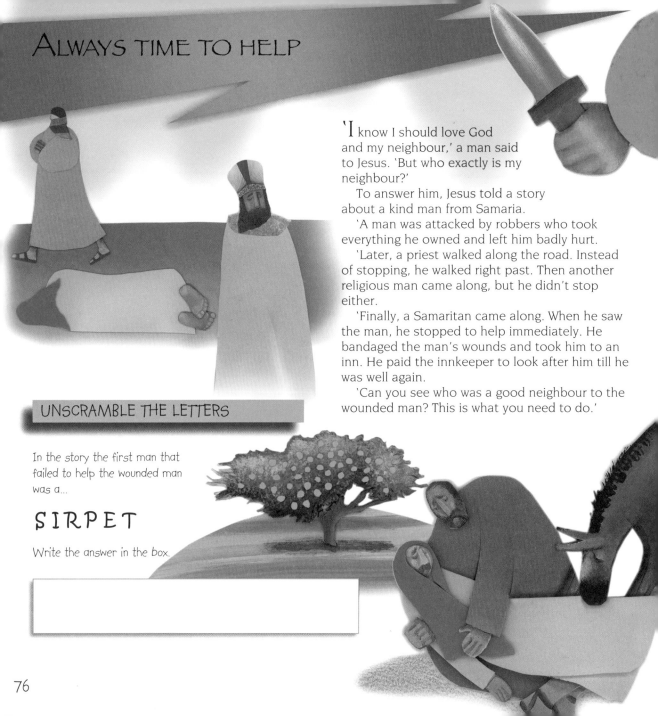

'I know I should love God and my neighbour,' a man said to Jesus. 'But who exactly is my neighbour?'

To answer him, Jesus told a story about a kind man from Samaria.

'A man was attacked by robbers who took everything he owned and left him badly hurt.

'Later, a priest walked along the road. Instead of stopping, he walked right past. Then another religious man came along, but he didn't stop either.

'Finally, a Samaritan came along. When he saw the man, he stopped to help immediately. He bandaged the man's wounds and took him to an inn. He paid the innkeeper to look after him till he was well again.

'Can you see who was a good neighbour to the wounded man? This is what you need to do.'

UNSCRAMBLE THE LETTERS

In the story the first man that failed to help the wounded man was a...

SIRPET

Write the answer in the box.

MAZE

Can you find your way to the inn?

START

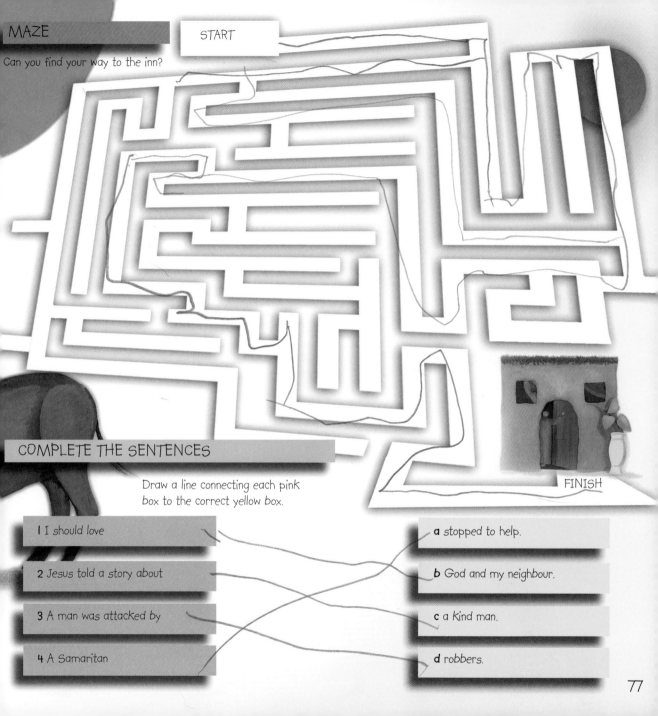

FINISH

COMPLETE THE SENTENCES

Draw a line connecting each pink box to the correct yellow box.

1 I should love	**a** stopped to help.
2 Jesus told a story about	**b** God and my neighbour.
3 A man was attacked by	**c** a kind man.
4 A Samaritan	**d** robbers.

REMEMBER TO SAY THANK YOU

In the time of Jesus there were people treated as outcasts because they had a bad skin disease. They couldn't live with their families or friends in case someone caught the disease from them.

So when Jesus saw a group of ten people huddled together and watching him, he knew what was wrong with them.

'Jesus, please help us,' they called out to him.

Jesus was not afraid of the men. He told them to go and show that they were healed—because they were!

The men could not believe it! Jesus had made their skin whole and well again.

One man, a Samaritan, came back and knelt at Jesus' feet, thanking God.

Jesus was happy to see the man well; he was happy that he had come to thank God. But he was sad that of all the ten men, only one wanted to say thank you.

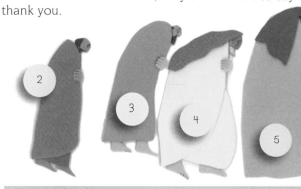

MATCH THE MEN

Match the shapes below to the ten men above.
Put the correct number in the circles.

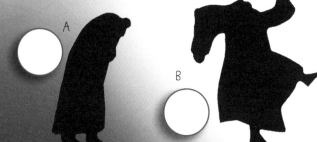

FIND THE RIGHT ANSWER

Choose the correct ending for each of the four sentences and write the answer in the box.

1 People with a skin disease:
A went to hospital.
B had to take lots of medicine.
C had to live far from their friends and family.

2 People with a skin disease:
A were very happy.
B were frightened and lonely.
C had lots of friends.

3 When Jesus met the ten men:
A he healed them.
B he told them not to bother him.
C he said he would help them another day.

4 When Jesus helped the ten men:
A they all hurried away.
B they all thanked God.
C only one thanked God.

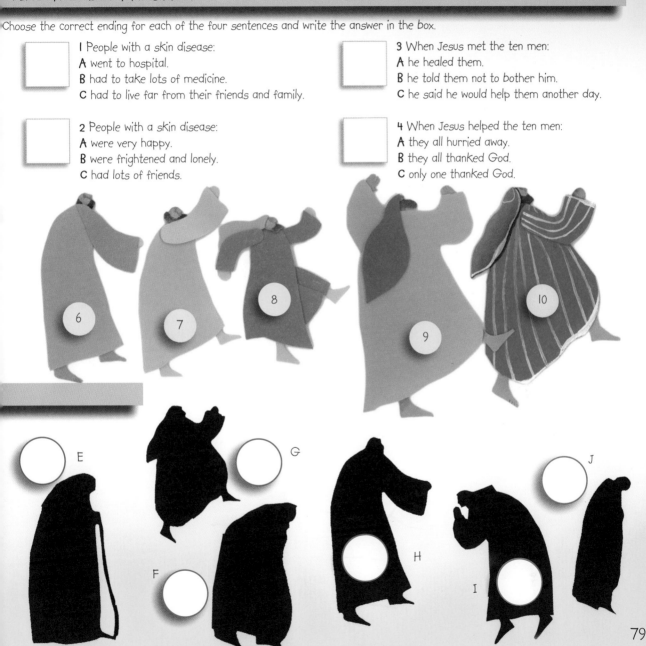

A FUNERAL TO GO TO

Jesus was friends with a man called Lazarus and his sisters, Mary and Martha. One day, the sisters sent a message to tell Jesus that Lazarus was seriously ill.

By the time Jesus reached their house, Lazarus had been buried for four days.

'I wish you had been here,' Martha told Jesus. 'I am sure my brother would still be alive.'

'Will you trust me, Martha?' Jesus asked. 'People who trust me will live for ever.'

'I know you are God's Son,' she replied. 'Wait while I fetch Mary.'

Mary, Martha and lots of their friends came to the place where Lazarus was buried. Jesus cried with them.

Then Jesus prayed and called Lazarus out from his grave. Everyone was amazed when they saw Lazarus—not as a dead person but very much alive! Jesus had brought him back from the dead.

MATCH THE SHAPES

Which three shapes are taken from the picture above?

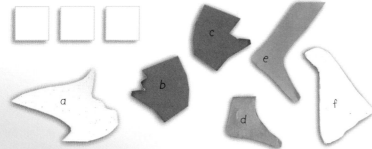

WORDSEARCH

Find the answers to the questions in the wordsearch.

1 Who was the friend who died?
2 What was the name of Martha's sister?
3 Who thought that Jesus was the son of God?
4 How many days had the man been in the tomb?

A	H	M	A	Z	E	W	Z
S	A	E	R	A	R	S	M
G	T	R	E	R	T	H	A
O	F	Y	T	U	N	E	R
L	O	P	C	S	N	H	T
D	N	N	M	E	P	B	H
F	O	U	R	M	M	E	A
O	U	R	P	A	A	R	S
M	L	A	Z	A	R	U	S
F	M	E	L	I	Y	L	S
T	A	Y	A	E	E	D	C

TIME WITH THE CHILDREN

Jesus had twelve special friends who were known as his disciples. They were all men. Jesus had other friends who were women, the wives or mothers or sisters of the people he knew, or people he had helped. Jesus also loved to be with children.

Mothers often brought their babies to be blessed by Jesus. Older children liked to be where Jesus was.

Sometimes the disciples discouraged them and said Jesus was too tired or too busy. But Jesus would welcome the children. He always had time for them.

'My kingdom is made up of people like these children,' Jesus said. 'Their faith is simple. Nothing gets in the way. They are able to love God and trust him, and God blesses them.'

QUESTIONS ABOUT CHILDREN.

Answer A or B.

1 Jesus was twelve when he was lost in... **A** Nazareth **B** Jerusalem

2 John the Baptist was the son of... **A** Zechariah and Elizabeth **B** Mary and Joseph

3 James and John were sons of... **A** Zebedee **B** Zacchaeus

4 Jesus healed the daughter of... **A** Jairus **B** The King

5 A boy offered to Jesus five pieces of bread and... **A** Two fish **B** Five fish

WHICH CHILD?

Caption the pictures with the right names. Read the clues below to help you select the right picture.

Cain killed Abel, his brother.

Jacob had a twin brother called Esau.

Moses was put in a basket on the River Nile.

Isaac was Abraham and Sarah's son.

Joseph was sold into slavery by his brothers.

Samuel heard God speak to him in the night.

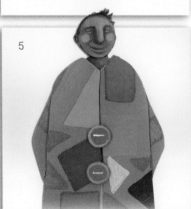

Is money a good thing?

What did Jesus think about money? Is it good to be rich? Is it bad to be poor?

'Once there was a man who did very well,' said Jesus. 'He did so well that he pulled down all his barns and built new, bigger, better buildings. He hoped that when it was done he could sit back and enjoy all his

money and be happy.

'But before he could do that, he died. All that he had worked for went to someone else. What a waste!

'Be happy with what you have,' Jesus said. 'Don't be greedy but share what you own. There is so much more to life than having more than someone else.'

COUNT THE CASH

1 How many coins are there in bag B?

2 Which bag holds the least coins?

UNSCRAMBLE THE WORDS

1 *Jesus said don't be* **DEGEYR**

2 *Jesus said it's good to* **AESHR**

C

3 Which bag holds
the most coins?

When Jesus went to Jericho, he was surrounded by crowds of noisy people. But Jesus could hear someone calling him above all the other voices. It was someone who needed his help.

'Who is that man calling me?' Jesus asked. 'Bring him here.'

So someone helped the man, the blind man begging at the side of the road, to find his way to Jesus. He was called Bartimaeus.

'How can I help you?' said Jesus.

'I just want to see!' said the blind man.

Jesus knew that the man had asked because he believed Jesus had the power to help him.

'It's OK,' said Jesus. 'Look, you can see!'

The man opened his eyes wide and smiled a big, wide smile. Jesus had healed him. The blind man could see!

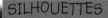

SILHOUETTES

Which *blue silhouette* exactly matches the man in yellow?

WORDSEARCH

Find the answers to the questions in the wordsearch.
1 Where did the blind man live?
2 How did the blind man get money?
3 Who was the only man who could help the blind man see?
4 What was the name of the blind man?

A H T U R B D
E A C S T A Y
G P B E N R S
O J E A N T F
J T G A P I A
E R G Y N M S
S E I L R A D
U E N R U E S
S Y G I A U E
F A A E E S T
J E R I C H O

SOUNDS

Put the sounds in this list in order.
Start with the loudest sound and end with the quietest sound.

cat purring
jet engine revving
bee buzzing
man talking
dog barking

1 [ ]

2 [ ]

3 [ ]

4 [ ]

5 [ ]

HIDING IN TREES

Jesus went into Jericho, smiling at all the people who were waiting to see him. There were crowds lining the way. They all wanted to talk to him.

Jesus could see a man climbing a fig tree a little way ahead. Jesus knew about Zacchaeus. He knew that he was a tax collector and that no one liked him. Jesus knew that Zacchaeus cheated people and stole from them.

Jesus also knew that Zacchaeus wanted to see him very much. So when Jesus reached the tree, he called up into the branches and invited himself to Zacchaeus' house.

The rest of the crowd started grumbling but Zacchaeus couldn't wait to meet Jesus. And from that day on, Zacchaeus was a changed man, generous and honest and kind.

'I came to help people just like Zacchaeus,' Jesus said.

WHAT'S HIDING IN THE TREE?

Find six animals hiding in the tree.

PLACE THE PUZZLE PIECES

A

C

B

1

2

3

COMPLETE THESE SENTENCES

People's lives changed when they met Jesus. Draw a line connecting each *blue box* with the correct *yellow box*.

| 1 Zacchaeus |
| 2 Bartimaeus |
| 3 Jairus |
| 4 Martha |
| 5 Ten men |
| 6 Peter |
| 7 A paralysed man |
| 8 A deaf man |

| **a** was able to walk again. |
| **b** was able to hear again. |
| **c** became a disciple. |
| **d** saw her brother brought back from the dead. |
| **e** became an honest, generous man. |
| **f** was healed of his blindness. |
| **g** were healed of leprosy. |
| **h** saw his daughter healed. |

89

Jesus taught that the life we live here on earth is not the end; and it matters how we live our lives.

'One day God will look at what everyone did with the time they spent on earth,' Jesus said. 'He will be pleased with some. He will say, "When I was hungry, you shared your food with me. When I needed clothes, you gave me some of yours. When I was in prison, you came to see me. When I was in hospital, you visited me."

'But to others, God will say, "You have not been kind; you do not belong here. You turned away when you saw I needed food or clothes. You always had something better to do than visit me in prison or hospital."

'The people will all ask, "But when? When did we do—or not do—any of these things?"

'And God will answer, "Every time you saw someone who needed help and gave it, then you did it for me. But every time you walked away and thought only of yourself, it was me who suffered too."'

BEING KIND

Fill in the missing words to identify two ways in which you can be kind.

1 Share...

F

2 Visit people in...

H

Crack the code and write these sentences in the boxes.

+ = a	# = e	* = i	< = o	♦ = u

1 L<V# y<♦r #n#m*#s.

2 B# k*nd +nd d<n't b<+st.

3 G*V# g#n#r<♦sly.

4 F<rg*V# p#<pl#.

Lazarus held a dinner party for Jesus and his friends in his home in Bethany. Martha had cooked a feast for them and they were all reclining at the low table.

No one noticed Mary at first. She knelt on the floor and poured the contents of a small jar over Jesus' feet. She washed off the dust and then used her long, thick hair to dry them.

The room was filled with the strong smell of the wonderful perfume. Then everyone turned to look.

'What a waste!' said Judas. 'We could have sold that perfume and given the money to the poor.'

But Jesus smiled at Mary.

'No, leave her alone. Mary has done something kind and good. I will not be with you for much longer. This is a beautiful gift.'

WHO BROUGHT GIFTS?

Can you unscramble the letters to discover some other people who had given Jesus some special gifts?

ISEW ENM

ROFM

ETH SETA

....

....

....

MATCH THE MONEY

Which sack is the same as the one pictured at the top of the page?

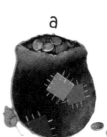

a

b

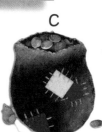

c

d

WHO DID WHAT?

There are two correct sentences that match each name below. Draw a line to join the right names and sentences.

Martha	1 cooked a feast for Jesus.
	2 was the sister of Mary.
Mary	3 gave Jesus a beautiful gift.
	4 was grumpy and ungenerous.
Lazarus	5 looked after the disciples' money.
	6 washed the feet of Jesus.
Judas	7 held a dinner party for Jesus.
	8 died but was brought back to life by Jesus.

WHERE DID IT HAPPEN?

Tick the right answer.

1 Where did Jesus turn water into wine?

CANADA ☐   CANA ☐   KANSAS ☐

2 Where did Jesus feed over 5000 people with bread and fish?

GAMBIA ☐   GALLIPOLI ☐   GALILEE ☐

3 Where did Jesus have a meal with Zacchaeus?

JERUSALEM ☐   JERICHO ☐   JERSEY ☐

4 Where did Jesus go to a dinner party with Lazarus and his sisters?

BUENOS AIRES ☐   BETHANY ☐   BETHSAIDA ☐

93

WHO IS JESUS?

People were smiling and cheering. Some were waving palm branches in the air. Others were laying cloaks under the donkey's feet.

What was happening? Who was this man, riding into Jerusalem on a donkey?

'It's Jesus!' someone in the crowd shouted above the noise. 'He's the teacher from Galilee everyone is talking about. They say no one has ever talked about God the way he does.'

'Did you see him heal the blind man?' someone else asked.

'I heard about a miracle with some bread and a couple of little fish—they say thousands of people shared a boy's lunch!'

'What about the lepers, then? Ten of them were healed and went back to live with their families.'

'So, he must have come for the Passover. Look! Here he is! Praise Jesus! Praise Jesus, the king.'

SPOT THE DIFFERENCE

There are six differences between the two pictures of Jesus riding the donkey. Put a circle round each one.

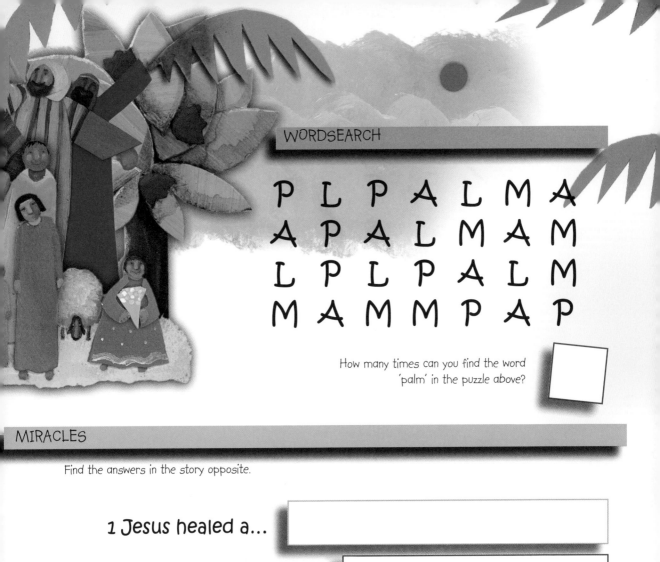

WORDSEARCH

P L P A L M A
A P A L M A M
L P L P A L M
M A M M P A P

How many times can you find the word 'palm' in the puzzle above?

MIRACLES

Find the answers in the story opposite.

1 Jesus healed a...

2 Jesus fed...

3 Jesus healed ten...

CHAOS IN THE TEMPLE

Now Jesus was in Jerusalem, he wanted to go to the temple to pray. He went there with his disciples, the twelve friends who had been travelling with him for the last few years.

The courtyard outside the temple was busy. But what Jesus saw shocked him. He watched people buying and selling animals for sacrifice as if this were a marketplace. And Jesus knew the people were being cheated there.

'Out!' Jesus shouted. 'This is God's house, a place to pray—not a place for people to steal from the poor!'

Then people came to Jesus to be healed. Smiling children gathered around him to hear what he said about God.

The religious leaders stood and watched. They were angry. They knew people were calling him a king, the Son of God himself.

WORDSEARCH

Can you find four words in this wordsearch which also appear in the story above?

WHERE IS IT?

Where was the temple?

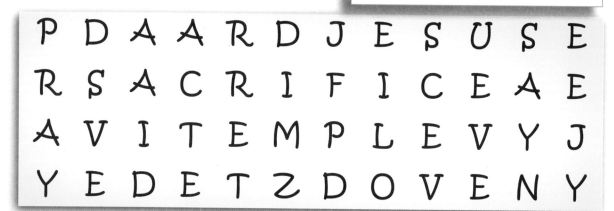

P	D	A	A	R	D	J	E	S	U	S	E
R	S	A	C	R	I	F	I	C	E	A	E
A	V	I	T	E	M	P	L	E	V	Y	J
Y	E	D	E	T	Z	D	O	V	E	N	Y

96

HAPPY
EASTER

EASTER CARDS

Cut out simple shapes like this from card or felt
to make your special Easter card.

JESUS AND HIS FRIENDS

Day by day, people followed Jesus to the temple and he answered their questions about God.

By Thursday, Jesus wanted to be alone with his friends. They went to eat together in an upstairs room in Jerusalem.

Before the meal, a servant usually washed their hot, dusty feet. But tonight, Jesus took water and a towel and did the job himself. Peter wasn't happy— Jesus was too important to do this!

'I want you to look after each other,' Jesus said. 'If people see you taking care of each other, they will know that you are special and that you are my friends.'

NAME THAT FRUIT

1   2   3

1

2

3

HOW MANY?

Look at the picture above and write the answer to these questions in the boxes.

a How many people have taken off their shoes to have their feet washed?

b How many people are wearing shoes?

c How many people are wearing more than one colour?

d Jesus had twelve special friends. How many are missing?

THE LAST SUPPER

'Love each other in the same way that I have loved you,' Jesus said.

'I would do anything you ask,' Peter said.

'Would you, Peter?' Jesus shook his head sadly. 'Before dawn tomorrow, when the cockerel crows, you will have said three times that you don't even know me.'

'I won't be with you much longer,' Jesus went on. 'Soon I will go to be in my Father's house. I will make a place ready for all of you—there is plenty of room there for everyone!'

Judas left the room quietly while Jesus was speaking. He had decided to betray Jesus to the religious leaders for 30 silver coins.

Jesus took some bread and a cup of wine and shared it with his friends.

'This is my body,' Jesus said. 'This is my blood. Remember me whenever you eat and drink together like this.'

COMPLETE THE WORDS

What did Jesus share with his friends at the last supper?

b _ _ _ _
and
w _ _ _

TRUE OR FALSE?

Write 'true' or 'false' next to each statement.

2 Jesus was going to God's house in heaven.

1 Jesus was going to Galilee.

3 There is not space for everyone in heaven.

UNSCRAMBLE THE WORDS

Which two people let Jesus down?

1 JDUSA

2 ETPRE

DESIGN A COIN

Draw a face on this blank 'coin' and add the date and a value.

FIND THE COINS

There should be 30 silver coins in the bag, but some of them are lost. Circle the ten coins you find hidden on these two pages.

Jesus prays in the garden

After they had eaten, Jesus went with his friends to a garden on the Mount of Olives.

He asked them to keep watch for him among the trees while he prayed.

Jesus was very sad. He asked God to help him.

'Father, I know that soon I must suffer and die. Please help me to be brave because I am very frightened. If there is any other way to save the people you love, then tell me now. Don't make me do this if there is any other way.'

Jesus returned to speak to his friends, but they had all fallen asleep. Jesus was even sadder now. He woke them, but it was too late.

HOW MANY?

1 How many men can you see keeping watch?

2 How many trees can you see in the garden?

3 How many of the men have their heads covered?

4 How many of the men are wearing blue?

102

FIND THE MISSING LETTER

Which letter has been missed out in these words from the story?

Aftr thy had atn, Jsus wnt with his frinds to a gardn on th Mount of Olivs.

WRITE A PRAYER

Jesus was sad and asked God to help him be brave. Write a prayer of your own here. Tell God about something that worries you.

TRUE OR FALSE?

If the statement is 'true' put a tick in the box; put a cross if it is false.

1 Jesus took his friends to a garden with olive trees in it.

2 Judas kept watch with him.

3 Jesus' friends could not stay awake.

103

Judas betrays Jesus

A crowd of angry men made their way towards Jesus and his friends. They were armed with clubs and swords. Judas was leading them.

'Hello, Master,' Judas said, stepping forward and kissing his cheek. This was the sign Judas had arranged beforehand so they would know who Jesus was.

Then guards surrounded Jesus and arrested him.

The disciples were terrified. They all ran away and left him.

Now the guards marched Jesus away to the house of the high priest where Jesus would be questioned. It was a long night.

QUIZ QUESTIONS

1 What were the angry men carrying?

2 How did Judas greet Jesus?

3 What did the other disciples do?

SPOT THE DIFFERENCE

Can you find five differences between these two pictures? Circle them on the picture below.

JIGSAW PIECES

Number the jigsaw pieces to show where they fit in the big picture.

1

2

3

4

5

PETER DENIES JESUS

Meanwhile Peter had followed at a distance and was now in the courtyard outside the house, waiting to see what would happen.

'Weren't you with Jesus?' asked a servant.

'You're one of Jesus' gang, aren't you?' asked another.

'You even have the same accent!' said a third.

'No! No! No!' said Peter. 'I don't know what you are talking about!'

Then the cockerel crowed. It was morning.

YES OR NO?

Jesus was questioned all night.
Write 'yes' or 'no' in the boxes to answer each question.

1 Was Jesus sent from God?

2 Had Jesus done anything wrong?

3 Did Jesus deserve to die?

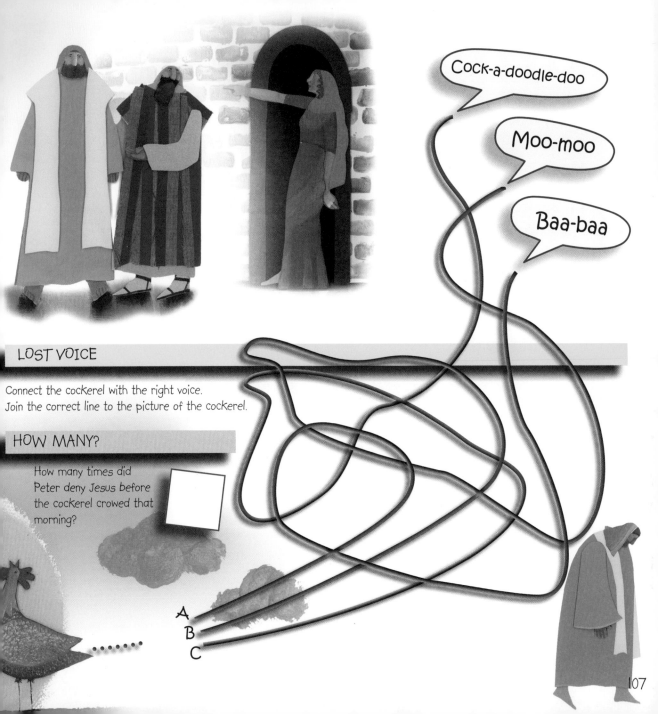

Cock-a-doodle-doo

Moo-moo

Baa-baa

LOST VOICE

Connect the cockerel with the right voice.
Join the correct line to the picture of the cockerel.

HOW MANY?

How many times did Peter deny Jesus before the cockerel crowed that morning?

A
B
C

THE ANGRY CROWD

TRUE OR FALSE?

Write 'true' or 'false' in the boxes.

1 Pontius Pilate was afraid of the crowd.

2 The religious leaders loved Jesus.

3 The crowd was stirred up.

Pontius Pilate was the Roman governor. He had heard about Jesus. He knew that the religious leaders wanted his death. But what had Jesus done wrong?

Eventually he went to the crowd who were waiting outside.

'It's Passover,' he said. 'I can set a prisoner free. Who should it be? This man, Jesus from Nazareth? Or Barabbas, the murderer?'

The crowd had been stirred up by the religious leaders.

'Barabbas!' they shouted. 'Free Barabbas!'

'Then what shall I do with Jesus?' Pilate asked again.

'Crucify him! Crucify him!' came the angry answer.

Pilate looked at the angry faces. Then he looked at Jesus.

'Take him away,' he said to the soldiers.

Draw a line connecting each blue box with the correct yellow box.

a Pontius Pilate was...

1 angry.

b The crowd was...

2 innocent.

c Barabbas was...

3 a Roman governor.

d Jesus was...

4 a murderer.

Tick the box if you would have released Jesus.

JESUS DIES ON A CROSS

The soldiers marched Jesus away. First they dressed him in a cloak and gave him a stick to hold in his hand. They forced a crown made out of prickly thorns on his head. They made fun of him, calling him 'King Jesus'. Then they beat him.

Finally they made him carry part of his cross to the place where criminals were executed. They crucified him there between two thieves.

Jesus' mother and John, his disciple, watched and cried while he suffered there.

'Look after my mother,' Jesus said to John. 'Treat John as your son,' he said to his mother.

Hours passed, until Jesus drew his last breath.

'It is finished!' he said. A soldier put a sword in his side to make sure that Jesus was dead.

WHO'S WHO?

Jesus told two people to take care of each other while he was on the cross. Write their names below.

CONNECT THE DOTS

Can you draw a cross by connecting these dots?

WORDSEARCH

M	H	A	E	K	N	F
A	S	D	H	M	F	H
D	I	T	A	S	E	U
S	D	E	N	O	E	I
H	E	N	D	H	T	O
E	A	X	S	N	G	P

Can you find the words in the puzzle above for the three places where Jesus was wounded?

ODD MEN OUT

Can you spot the two soldiers who are not wearing the correct uniform?

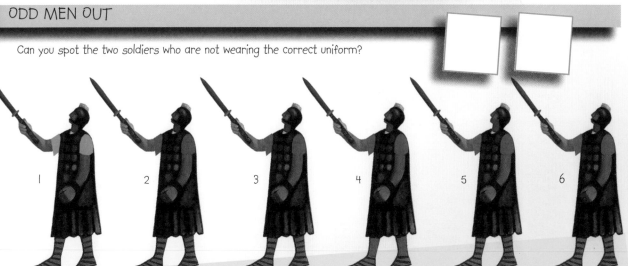

1   2   3   4   5   6

JESUS IS BURIED

Jesus' friends could hardly believe what had happened. The day before Jesus had been with them, alive and well. Now he was dead.

One of his followers had a grave ready for his own death. He went to Pontius Pilate and asked if he could take down Jesus' body and bury him before nightfall.

Then he and another friend wound a clean linen sheet around his body and buried Jesus in the grave, a rock tomb in a garden.

They rolled a heavy stone across the entrance.

Some of the women, who had also been friends of Jesus, followed and saw where he was buried.

ANIMAL SEARCH

Can you find the answers to the three questions below in the wordsearch? Write the answers in the boxes.

3 Which animal is sleeping?

2 Which animal is green?

3 Which creature has no legs?

```
M  I  T  N  B
S  L  D  M  E
T  A  O  S  S
O  T  G  K  N
N  E  E  M  A
F  R  O  G  K
P  D  A  O  E
```

1 Write down two creatures in the picture that can fly.

2 Write down two creatures in the picture that can jump.

THE FIRST EASTER MORNING

The next day was the sabbath day, a special day of rest. Very early on Sunday morning, one of the women, whose name was Mary Magdalene, went to the garden to see the place where they had buried Jesus.

When she saw that the heavy stone had been rolled away, she peeped inside. Jesus' body was not there! The tomb was empty.

Mary was very upset. She ran to tell Peter and John that someone had stolen the body. The two friends went to look for themselves but then they left Mary weeping.

Someone else saw her crying. Mary thought at first that the gardener was there. She looked up through her tears.

'Mary,' said a kind voice.

'Jesus!' said Mary. She knew that voice at once. Here was Jesus, very much alive!

COLOUR IT IN

Colour in the flowers.

WORDSEARCH

Which four flowers can you find in the wordsearch?

```
A  S  O  R  D  A  I  S  Y  E  I  L  T  W  R
S  Y  I  E  G  B  U  T  T  E  R  C  U  P  O
D  O  T  D  H  U  G  R  K  T  U  P  M  O  S
I  L  R  G  U  R  P  O  T  C  M  C  J  S  E
S  O  T  R  T  U  L  I  P  L  N  M  X  E  K
```

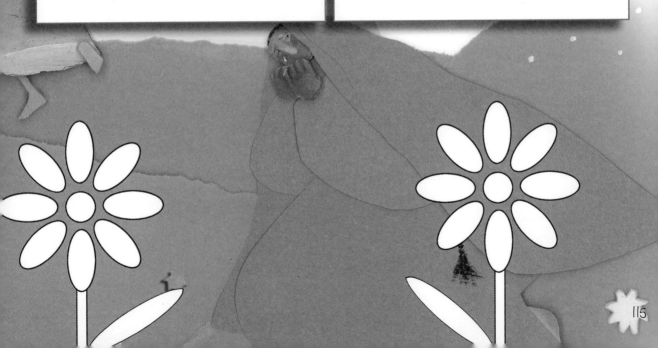

115

Jesus is Alive!

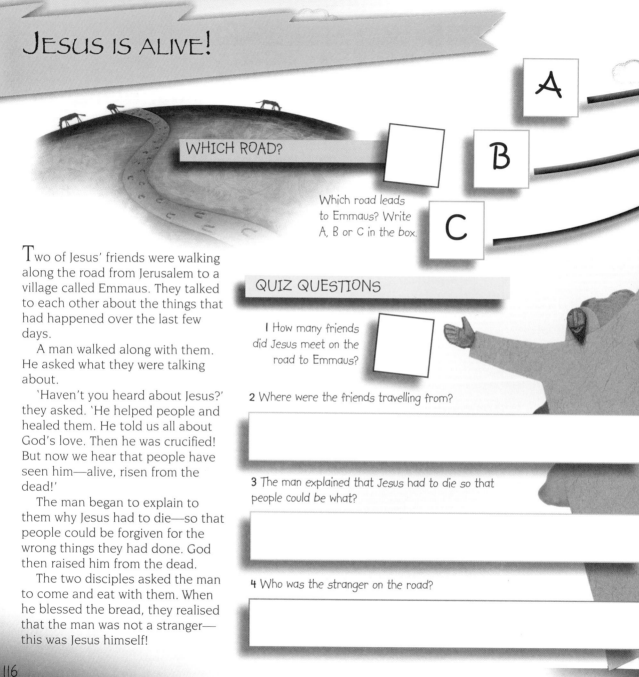

WHICH ROAD?

Which road leads to Emmaus? Write A, B or C in the box.

A

B

C

Two of Jesus' friends were walking along the road from Jerusalem to a village called Emmaus. They talked to each other about the things that had happened over the last few days.

A man walked along with them. He asked what they were talking about.

'Haven't you heard about Jesus?' they asked. 'He helped people and healed them. He told us all about God's love. Then he was crucified! But now we hear that people have seen him—alive, risen from the dead!'

The man began to explain to them why Jesus had to die—so that people could be forgiven for the wrong things they had done. God then raised him from the dead.

The two disciples asked the man to come and eat with them. When he blessed the bread, they realised that the man was not a stranger— this was Jesus himself!

QUIZ QUESTIONS

1 How many friends did Jesus meet on the road to Emmaus?

2 Where were the friends travelling from?

3 The man explained that Jesus had to die so that people could be what?

4 Who was the stranger on the road?

THE DISCIPLES MEET JESUS

The disciples were afraid and were together in a locked room.

But suddenly Jesus was there with them!

'Don't be afraid,' he said. 'It's really me. I was dead but now I am alive!'

Jesus showed them the wounds in his hands, feet and side. Then he asked if he could have something to eat.

Thomas was not with the others when Jesus came. He would not believe that Jesus had been there with them.

'I can't believe unless I see him myself,' said Thomas.

A week later, Jesus came to them again when Thomas was there.

'Here I am, Thomas. Now do you believe that I am alive?' said Jesus.

Thomas saw him and believed!

QUIZ QUESTIONS

1 How many wounds did Jesus have?

2 Who struggled to believe?

3 Which disciple was no longer with the others?

SPOT THE DIFFERENCE

Can you find all five differences in these two pictures?
Draw an arrow from each number to a picture difference.

1   2   3   4   5

MATCH THE SHAPES

Tick the shapes that match those in the main picture on page 118.

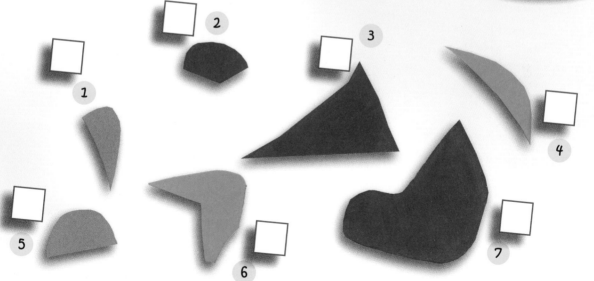

1

2

3

4

5

6

7

BREAKFAST WITH JESUS

'I'm going fishing,' said Peter to his friends one evening.

Seven of the disciples spent a quiet night on Lake Galilee. By morning they had caught nothing. A man stood on the shore watching the boat come in.

'Throw your net on the right side!' he called to them.

When they did, the net was so full of wriggling fish that they could not haul it in! Then the men realised that the man was Jesus. Peter jumped into the cool water and swam to shore.

They all knew that this was the man they had seen crucified, dead and buried—but here he was, Jesus, eating bread and fish at the lakeside with them.

QUIZ QUESTIONS

Which two types of food did Jesus share with his friends?

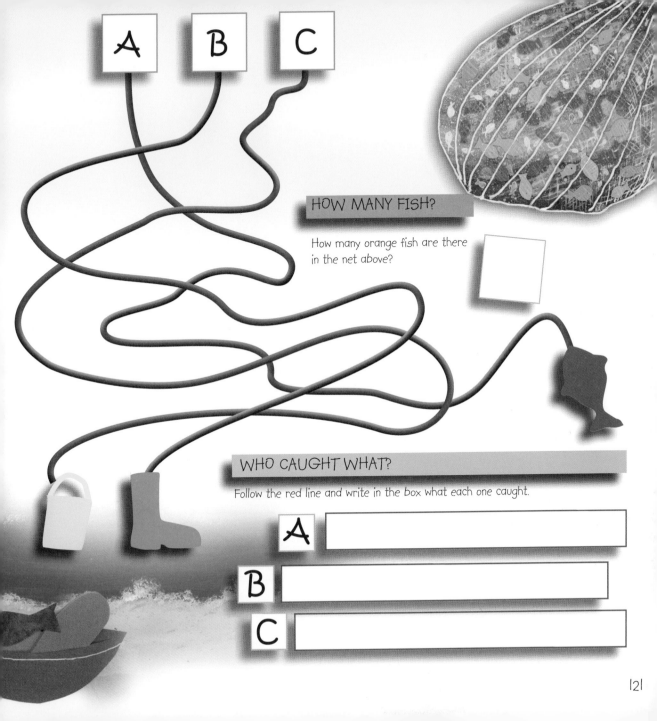

HOW MANY FISH?

How many orange fish are there in the net above?

WHO CAUGHT WHAT?

Follow the red line and write in the box what each one caught.

A

B

C

THE ASCENSION

For the next 40 days, Jesus met the disciples and all those who were his friends many times. Sometimes huge crowds saw Jesus and listened to him talking about God. No one doubted that this really was Jesus raised from the dead.

Then Jesus met them for one last time. His message was clear.

'Go into the world,' Jesus said. 'Baptise people from every country and teach them all the things I have taught you. I will always be there to help you.'

Then Jesus left them and returned to heaven.

COMPLETE THE SENTENCE

1 Crowds of people saw Jesus after	a to be with God in heaven.
2 Jesus said, 'Baptise people	b be there to help you.'
3 Jesus said, 'I will always	c from every country.'
4 Jesus left his disciples and returned	d to love one another.
5 Jesus taught his disciples	e he rose from the dead.

Only five of these jigsaw pieces fit in the picture above. Write the matching number beside the five that fit and put a cross next to those that do not fit.

A B C D E

F G H I J

123

THE HOLY SPIRIT COMES

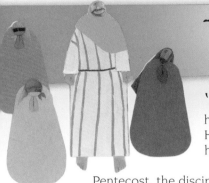

'Go to Jerusalem,' Jesus had told his friends. 'The Holy Spirit will come to help you.'

So on the Feast of Pentecost, the disciples waited. Then the Holy Spirit came to them like wind and fire. Jesus had promised to help them; now they knew that it was true.

Peter stood up bravely and talked to a huge crowd of people. Thousands believed that God would forgive their sins because Jesus had died in their place on the cross. Thousands of people became Christians as each one heard the news that Jesus had died and rose from the dead at Easter.

TWO THINGS

What are the two things that describe what the Holy Spirit is like?

w	f
....	....

MATCH THE SHAPES

Put the correct letter in the boxes to show where each head covering belongs.

QUIZ QUESTION

The Bible sometimes describes the Holy Spirit as a bird. Artists often draw the Holy Spirit in this way. What kind of bird is it?

d ....

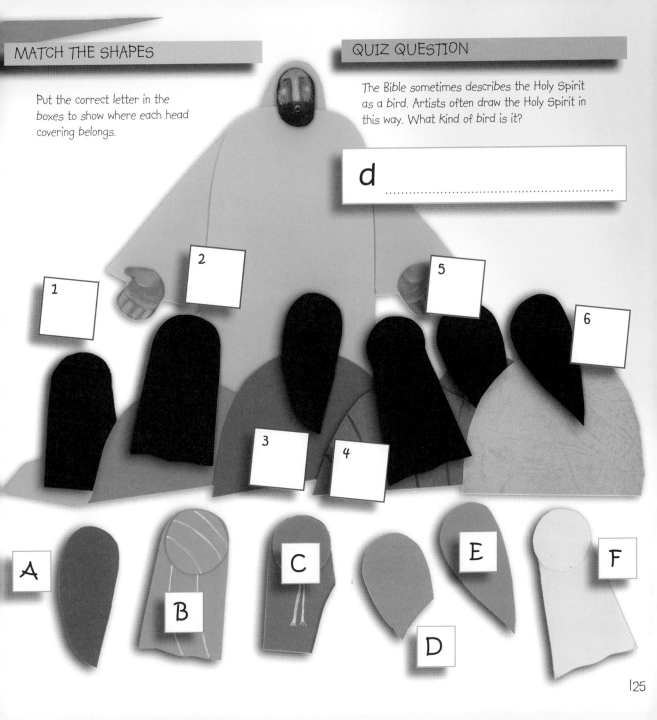

1

2

5

6

3

4

A

B

C

E

F

D

125

The new Christians learned to love as Jesus had taught them. They shared everything they had.

Jesus' friends were also able to heal people in the same way that Jesus had. A man who couldn't walk asked them for money outside the temple.

'We don't have any money,' Peter told him, 'but Jesus has given us power to heal you!'

Then the man stood up and walked.

'Look, I can walk!' he told everyone. 'God has healed me!'

WORDSEARCH

Find four parts of the body that Jesus healed in the wordsearch and write them in the boxes below.

```
S E S K L E H E E S Y R
D S F I E S L I D U R F
F O M N G A E E G A S E
E I E Y E S G G E A R S
Y S K I N X S H V E R J
```

L

E

E

S

MATCH THE MIRACLES

Put the number of the miracle in the box on the picture below.

A Jesus healed a deaf man.

B Jesus healed a blind beggar.

C Jesus healed Jairus' daughter.

D Jesus healed ten lepers.

E Jesus healed a lame man.

THE ROAD TO DAMASCUS

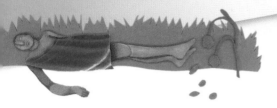

Saul hated the new Christians. He had watched a good man named Stephen die because he followed Jesus. Now he wanted to see all the others put in prison.

On his way to Damascus he was blinded by a bright light.

'Saul, Saul,' said a voice, 'what are you doing?

I am Jesus, the one you are so angry with. You are hurting my friends and that hurts me,' said Jesus.

Ananias met Saul in Damascus.

'Jesus has sent me to help you,' he told Saul. Ananias healed Saul's blindness. Then Saul received the Holy Spirit and was baptised. Now he was a changed man, and people called him Paul. But the religious leaders had become Paul's enemies. They planned to kill him. His new friends, the Christians, helped him escape in a basket down the city walls.

WHICH NAME?

1 Saul became a new man after he met Jesus. People even gave him a different name. Tick the right name in the list.

Saul

Jacob ☐

Paul ☐

Mark ☐

2 Which of these names were given to Jesus? Mark the right names with a tick.

Jesus

Lord ☐

John ☐

Ananias ☐

Christ ☐

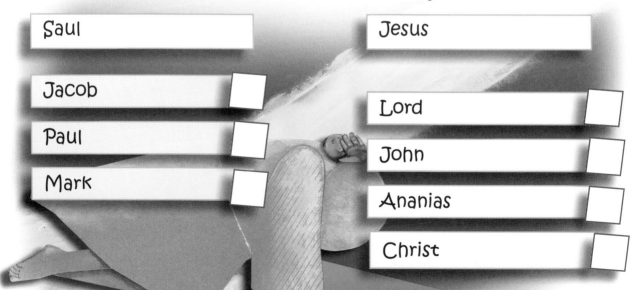

WHO SAID THIS?

'You are hurting my friends and that hurts me.'

WHICH ROAD?

Which road leads to Damascus? Follow the red line and write A, B or C in the box.

A

B

C

129

THE MAN IN THE CHARIOT

Philip's life had also been changed by the Holy Spirit.

'Go to Gaza,' he was told. 'You will see a man in a chariot who needs your help.'

The man was reading from a scroll. Philip was able to help him understand what he was reading. It was about Jesus and how he had been crucified and raised from the dead by a miracle, and how his friends had received God's forgiveness for all the bad things they had done.

'Can you baptise me?' the man asked. 'I want to be a Christian too.'

So Philip baptised the man in a stream nearby. The man went back to Ethiopia where he lived, and told the people there all about Jesus.

WHERE DID THE MAN COME FROM?

Tick the right answer.

1 Africa ☐   2 South America ☐   3 North America ☐

4 Australia ☐   5 Europe ☐   6 Asia ☐

BREAK THE CODE

Use the code to write down the three messages below.

● = a   * = e   ✦ = i   ✿ = o   ✚ = u

1 G✿ t✿ G✿z✿ ●nd f✦nd ● m●n wh✿ n**ds y✿✚r h*lp.

. . . .

. . . .

2 J*s✚s h●s b**n r●✦s*d fr✿m th* d*●d.

. . . .

. . . .

3 Y✿✚ c●n rec*✦v* G✿d's f✿rg✦v*n*ss.

. . . .

. . . .

PETER'S STRANGE VISION

Peter went to the home of a captain in the Roman army called Cornelius.

Peter had had a vision. He had seen a blanket, filled with every kind of creature, lowered in front of him. Then God had told him to eat. But some of the creatures were foods forbidden to God's people.

'It's OK; God has made them good,' Peter was told.

At first Peter did not understand the vision. But soon it became clear that God was telling Peter that everyone was welcome in God's family, even if they were not Jewish.

So when Cornelius asked to meet Peter, he told him all about Jesus—and he and his family were baptised as Christians.

PAIRS

Draw a line to join pairs of animals. How many pairs can you find?

Which of these puzzle pieces fit in picture A and which fit in picture B? Write A or B in the boxes.

1

2

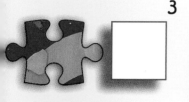

3

4

PEOPLE PRAY FOR PETER

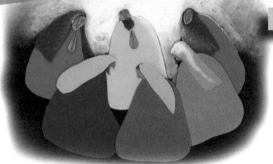

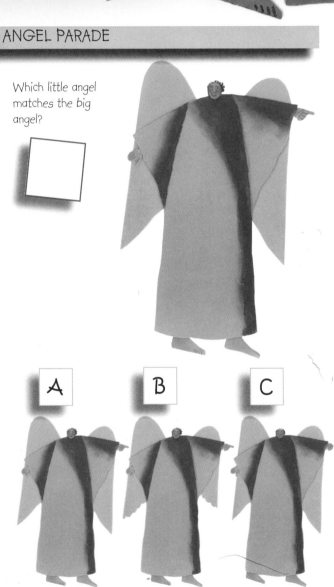

ANGEL PARADE

Which little angel matches the big angel?

A B C

It was dangerous to be a Christian. James, one of the first disciples, had been executed. Now Peter had been put in prison.

King Herod was planning a public trial to warn others not to become Christians. Peter was chained between two soldiers in the prison.

Peter's friends prayed that God would help him. God answered their prayers.

'Wake up!' It was an angel inside Peter's prison cell. 'Put on your shoes. Wrap yourself in your cloak.'

Peter felt the chains fall from his wrists. He saw doors open and close by a miracle! The soldiers were still asleep when Peter followed the angel into the street.

His friends heard a knocking on the door. Rhoda went to answer it, but she couldn't believe what she heard—it was Peter! God had answered their prayers. God had set Peter free from the prison and he was safe with them again.

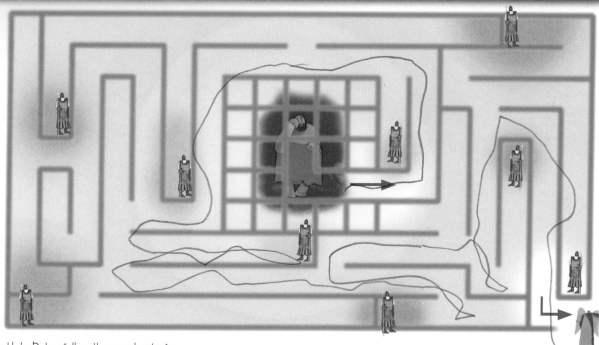

Help Peter follow the angel out of the prison.

HOW MANY?

How many mice can you count in Peter's prison cell? Write the number in the box.

STORMS AND SHIPWRECKS

Paul went from country to country telling everyone about Jesus so they could know him as he did. Sometimes he was welcomed and churches were started; at other times he was attacked or beaten and put in prison.

Finally, Paul was sent to Rome to stand trial there.

While he was on the ship, there was a terrible storm. But God kept all the people on board safe. Although the ship was wrecked, the passengers were able to swim to the shore or drift in, clinging to the wreckage.

Paul stayed on the island of Malta for three months, healing people and telling them about Jesus.

Paul was placed under house arrest in Rome but he was still able to write to the new churches, reminding everyone that they should take care of each other.

The Christian church had only just begun. Soon it was to spread all around the world.

Sort out the letters below and write four things that might come in a storm.

1   I W D N

2   N R I A

SPOT THE DIFFERENCE

Circle the six differences between the two pictures on the picture below.

3   L F O D O

4   A I H L

A N S W E R S

6-7 A MIRACLE IN THE TEMPLE

LOST AND FOUND
1 His voice; 2 A baby

HOW MANY NAMES?
Five

```
E M P E T E R G
V N A A J O H N
E E U R M M T L
Z N L U K E H S
```

THE BABY'S NAME
John

MATCH THE TEMPLE
A

8-9 MARY AND THE ANGEL

PUZZLE
A 9; B 10; C 5; D 8; E 4; F 2; G 3;
H 6; J 1; K 7

10-11 A VISIT TO ELIZABETH

THE SHORT ROAD
A

MAKE THE LINK
1 D; 2 C; 3 B; 4 A

JOBS
1 Shepherd; 2 Soldier; 3 King;
4 Priest

12-13 JOSEPH DREAMS OF ANGELS

SHADOWS
1 B; 2 D; 3 E; 4 A; 5 C

SPOT THE DIFFERENCE

14-15 THE ROMAN CENSUS

SPOT THE DIFFERENCE

MISSING LETTERS
1 e (Bethlehem); 2 m (Emperor);
3 p (Joseph); 4 r (Mary);
5 m (Romans)

HOW MANY?
a 3; b 1; c 5; d 3

16-17 NO ROOM AT THE INN

SPOT THE DIFFERENCE

TRUE OR FALSE?
1 ✗; 2 ✓; 3 ✗; 4 ✓; 5 ✗

18-19 A VERY STARRY NIGHT

MATCH THE SHAPE
Manger B; Donkey C

FIND THE NAMES
1 Jesus; 2 Joseph

```
J M J O S E P H U
A A D A V I D M J
M T P J C R L A O
E T L J E S U S H
S M A N G E R H R
```

20-21 SHEPHERDS ON THE HILLSIDE

TRUE OR FALSE?
1 ✗; 2 ✓; 3 ✗; 4 ✓

22-23 THE BABY IN THE MANGER

BREAK THE CODE
1 The shepherds ran to Bethlehem.
2 They found the baby lying in a manger.
3 They praised God because Jesus had been born.

24-25 SIMEON MEETS JESUS

CONNECTIONS
a-4; b-1; c-2; d-3

MISSING WORDS
1 peace; 2 Jesus; 3 save

26-27 A BRIGHT NEW STAR

QUIZ
1 the east; 2 by camel; 3 a new star;
4 a King

SPOT THE DIFFERENCE

28-29 THE KING IN THE PALACE

THE KING'S THINGS
1 throne; 2 palace; 3 crown

WHICH WAY?
B

DRAW A CROWN

30-31 WISE MEN WORSHIP

WHICH WAY?
1 West; 2 East; 3 South

32–33 A VERY BAD DREAM

QUESTIONS AND ANSWERS
1 shepherds; 2 east; 3 Herod;
4 Joseph; 5 manger; 6 baby;
7 census; 8 angels; 9 star

34–35 ESCAPE TO EGYPT

WHO DREAMED WHAT?
a 2; b 3; c 4; d 1

WHAT'S MISSING?

36–37 EXILES IN EGYPT

WHERE DID THEY GO?
1 B; 2 C; 3 B

CAPTION THE PICTURES
1 Moses; 2 Joseph; 3 Joseph;
4 Abraham and Sarah

38–39 A HOME IN NAZARETH

WHICH WAY?

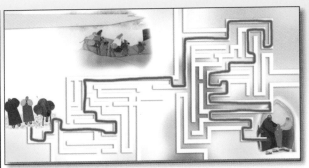

40–41 LOST AND FOUND

FIND JESUS

42–43 JOHN THE BAPTIST

WHAT DID HE SAY?
1 ✓; 2 ✓; 3 ✗; 4 ✗

WHAT FOOD IS THIS?
Honey

44–45 JESUS IS BAPTISED

COMPLETE THE SENTENCE
1 d; 2 e; 3 b; 4 a; 5 c

TRUE OR FALSE?
1 ✓; 2 ✓; 3 ✗

46–47 JESUS IS TESTED

WHO IS THIS?
1 Eve; 2 Adam

FILL IN THE MISSING WORDS
1 Bread; 2 Son 3 me, see

48–49 JESUS MAKES FRIENDS

WHAT HAPPENED NEXT?
2 ✓

PUZZLE PIECES
Picture A: 1, 3, 7, 8
Picture B: 2, 4, 5, 6

TANGLED LINES
A boot; B bucket; C fish

50–51 TWELVE SPECIAL FRIENDS

TRUE OR FALSE?
1 ✗; 2 ✗; 3 ✓; 4 ✗

ODD ONE OUT
Peter, James, Philip, John and
Andrew were fishermen.
The odd one out is Matthew; he was
a tax collector.

PUZZLE PIECES
A 4; B 5; C 2; D 1; E 3

JESUS' FRIENDS
1 12; 2 Judas

52–53 INVITATION TO A WEDDING

WEDDING GUESTS
1 B; 2 E; 3 I; 4 H; 5 C; 6 G

WHAT HAPPENED WHERE?
1 d; 2 f; 3 e; 4 a; 5 c; 6 b

54–55 A CROWD COMES TO LISTEN

WORDSEARCH
1 Peter; 2 four; 3 roof; 4 walk

```
A O F A T E L E E N H L A E C
S M O M R T A A E R E D S L I
G F O U R C Z A R W H Z D E O
O T E R E M A Y T A B E U R D
L H U Y Y I R L N L E D L O Z
D A L P E T E R N K R P O O S
L T M N R H S I P S O F S R R
```

FIND THE MATCH
A

139

56–57
SITTING ON THE HILLSIDE

JESUS SAID
1 Don't worry; 2 Love your enemies

COMPLETE THE SENTENCES
1–C; 2–D; 3–E; 4–B; 5–A

MORE THINGS JESUS SAID
1 God; 2 hurt you

58–59 TIME TO PRAY

COMPLETE THE PRAYER
1 name; 2 done; 3 bread;
4 forgive; 5 temptation;
6 power; 7 Amen

60–61 A FRIEND IN CAPERNAUM

SPOT THE DIFFERENCE

CHOOSE THE RIGHT PIECE
A A3; B B2; C C1

62–63 A SUDDEN STORM

WHAT HAPPENED NEXT?
4

WHO'S IN THE BOAT?
1 ✗; 2 ✓; 3 ✓; 4 ✗; 5 ✓; 6 ✗

HOW MANY FISH?
1 ✓; 2 ✗; 3 ✗; 4 ✓

64–65 A WORRIED FATHER

MAZE

66–67 A PICNIC BY THE LAKE

MATCH THE BASKETS
A 5; B 12; C 1; D 8; E 4; F 3; G 10;
H 2; I 9; J 7; K 11; L 6

HOW MANY?
1 9; 2 3

NUMBER QUIZ
1 12; 2 5; 3 2; 4 12; 5 31

UNTANGLE THE LETTERS
1 Philip; 2 Andrew

68–69 A NIGHT-TIME BOAT TRIP

SPOT THE DIFFERENCE

WORDSEARCH
1 Galilee; 2 Jesus; 3 Peter;
4 evening; 5 help

```
A O T L Y E L A E N P E E Z S
S M F E P Y M I J E E W R E D
G F O G A L I L E E T S R D U
O T N M T E P R S H E L P P L
E V E N I N G U O S R E L F O
D A U R A T L I S U A T D A S
```

70–71
NO SOUND FROM THE BIRDS

SPOT THE BIRDS
1 robin; 2 eagle; 3 parrot

NOISES
oink: pig; **moo**: cow

MIRACLES
1 wine; 2 walk; 3 servant; 4 storm;
5 fish; 6 water

72–73 STORIES OF WISE AND FOOLISH

MISTAKES
Be like the wise man who built his house on ~~seaside~~ rock. It took a long time and it ~~was~~ hard work—but when the ~~elephant came~~ he was warm and safe inside.
    'Don't be like the foolish man! He didn't like ~~unpaid~~ work. He built on the ~~jelly~~ where it was easy to dig. It didn't take him long to build—but as soon as the storm came, his ~~mouse~~ crumbled around him and was blown away.

TRUE OR FALSE?
True: 2, 3, 5, 6, 8

74–75
STORIES OF LOST AND FOUND

WHAT HAPPENED NEXT?
1 ✗; 2 ✗; 3 ✗; 4 ✓; 5 ✗

FIND THE LOST SHEEP

76–77 ALWAYS TIME TO HELP

UNSCRAMBLE THE LETTERS
priest

MAZEs

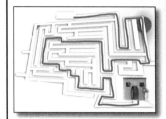

COMPLETE THE SENTENCES
1–b; 2–c; 3–d; 4–a

78–79
REMEMBER TO SAY THANK YOU

MATCH THE MEN
A 3; B 8; C 7; D 9; E 5; F 4; G 10;
H 6; I 1; J 2

FIND THE RIGHT ANSWER
1 C; 2 B; 3 A; 4 C

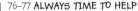

80-81 A FUNERAL TO GO TO

MATCH THE SHAPES
b, d, f

WORDSEARCH
1 Lazarus; 2 Mary; 3 Martha;
4 four

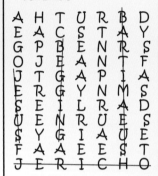

82-83
TIME WITH THE CHILDREN

QUESTIONS ABOUT CHILDREN
1 B; 2 A; 3 A; 4 A; 5 A

WHICH CHILD?
1 Jacob; 2 Samuel;
3 Moses; 4 Cain;
5 Joseph; 6 Isaac

84-85
IS MONEY A GOOD THING?

COUNT THE CASH
1 19; 2 c; 3 a

UNSCRAMBLE THE WORDS
1 greedy; 2 share

86-87
WAITING BY THE ROADSIDE

SILHOUETTES
D

WORDSEARCH
1 Jericho; 2 begging; 3 Jesus;
4 Bartimaeus

SOUNDS
1 jet engine revving; 2 dog barking;
3 man talking; 4 bee buzzing;
5 cat purring

88-89 HIDING IN TREES

WHAT'S HIDING IN THE TREE?
cat, frog, mouse, chicken, bird,
grasshopper

PLACE THE PUZZLE PIECES
1 C; 2 B; 3 A

COMPLETE THESE SENTENCES
1-e; 2-f; 3-h; 4-d; 5-g; 6-c; 7-a; 8-b

90-91 VISITS TO HOSPITAL

BEING KIND
1 food; 2 hospital

BREAK THE CODE
1 Love your enemies.
2 Be kind and don't boast.
3 Give generously. 4 Forgive people.

92-93 AN EXPENSIVE TREAT

WHO BROUGHT GIFTS?
Wise men from the east

MATCH THE MONEY
b

WHO DID WHAT?
Martha: 1, 2; **Mary:** 3, 6;
Lazarus: 7, 8; **Judas:** 4, 5

WHERE DID IT HAPPEN?
1 Cana; 2 Galilee; 3 Jericho;
4 Bethany

94-95 WHO IS JESUS?

SPOT THE DIFFERENCE

WORDSEARCH
5

MIRACLES
1 blind man; 2 thousands of people;
3 lepers

96-97 CHAOS IN THE TEMPLE

WORDSEARCH

P D A A R D JESUS E
R SACRIFICE A E
A V I TEMPLE V Y J
Y E D E T Z D O V E N Y

WHERE IS IT?
Jerusalem

98-99 JESUS AND HIS FRIENDS

NAME THAT FRUIT
1 orange; 2 apple; 3 grapes

HOW MANY?
a 7; b 3; c 5; d 2

100-101 THE LAST SUPPER

FIND THE COINS

COMPLETE THE WORDS
bread, wine

TRUE OR FALSE
1 false; 2 true; 3 false

UNSCRAMBLE THE WORDS
1 Judas; 2 Peter

102-103
JESUS PRAYS IN THE GARDEN

HOW MANY?
1 9; 2 2; 3 6; 4 3

FIND THE MISSING LETTER
e

TRUE OR FALSE
1 ✓; 2 ✗; 3 ✓

104-105 JUDAS BETRAYS JESUS

QUIZ QUESTIONS
1 clubs and swords; 2 with a kiss;
3 ran away

SPOT THE DIFFERENCE

JIGSAW PIECES
1 B; 2 D; 3 A; 4 C; 5 E

106-107 PETER DENIES JESUS

YES OR NO?
1 yes; 2 no; 3 no

LOST VOICE
C

HOW MANY?
3

108-109 THE ANGRY CROWD

TRUE OR FALSE?
1 true; 2 false; 3 true

WHO WAS WHAT?
a–3; b–1; c–4; d–2

110-111 JESUS DIES ON A CROSS

WHO'S WHO?
Mary, John

CONNECT THE DOTS

WORDSEARCH

M H A E K N F
A S D H M F H
D I T A S E U
S D E N O E I
H E N D H T O
E A X S N G P

ODD MEN OUT
1 and 4

112-113 JESUS IS BURIED

ANIMAL SEARCH
1 dog; 2 frog; 3 snake

M I T N B
S L D M E
T A O S S
O T G K N
N E E M A
F R O G K
P D A O E

FIND THE CREATURES
1 butterfly and bird;
2 frog and grasshopper

114-115
THE FIRST EASTER MORNING

WORDSEARCH
Daisy, buttercup, tulip, rose

A S O R D A I S Y E I L T W R
S Y I E G B U T T E R C U P O
D O T D H U G R K T U P M O S
I L R G U R P O T C M C J S E
S O T R T U L I P L N M X E K

116-117 JESUS IS ALIVE!

WHICH ROAD?
B

QUIZ QUESTIONS
1 2; 2 Jerusalem; 3 forgiven; 4 Jesus

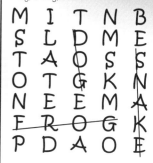

118-119
THE DISCIPLES MEET JESUS

QUIZ QUESTIONS
1 5; 2 Thomas; 3 Judas

SPOT THE DIFFERENCE

MATCH THE SHAPES
1, 3, 6, 7

120-121 BREAKFAST WITH JESUS

QUIZ QUESTIONS
bread and fish

HOW MANY FISH?
9

WHO CAUGHT WHAT?
A the fish; B the boot; C the bucket

122-123 THE ASCENSION

COMPLETE THE SENTENCE
1-e; 2-c; 3-b; 4-a; 5-d

PLACE THE PUZZLE PIECES
1 C; 2 J; 3 D; 4 F; 5 B

124-125 THE HOLY SPIRIT COMES

TWO THINGS
wind; fire

MATCH THE SHAPES
1 C; 2 B; 3 A; 4 F; 5 D; 6 E

QUIZ QUESTION
dove

126-127 THE POWER TO HEAL

WORDSEARCH

MATCH THE MIRACLES
1 D; 2 C; 3 A; 4 E; 5 B

128-129
THE ROAD TO DAMASCUS

WHICH NAME?
1 Paul; 2 Lord, Christ

WHO SAID THIS?
Jesus

WHICH ROAD?
A

130-131
THE MAN IN THE CHARIOT

WHERE DID THE MAN COME
FROM?
Africa

BREAK THE CODE
1 Go to Gaza and find a man who
needs your help.
2 Jesus has been raised from the
dead.
3 You can receive God's forgiveness.

132-133
PETER'S STRANGE VISION

PAIRS
5

A OR B?
1 B; 2 B; 3 A; 4 A

134-135 PEOPLE PRAY FOR PETER

ANGEL PARADE
A

HOW MANY?
7

FIND THE RIGHT PATH

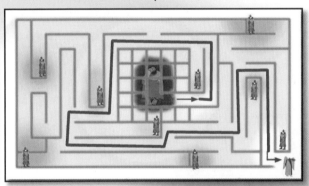

136-137 STORMS AND
SHIPWRECKS

SPOT THE DIFFERENCE

UNJUMBLE THE LETTERS
1 wind; 2 rain; 3 flood; 4 hail

Barnabas for Children®

Barnabas for Children® is a registered word mark
and the logo is a registered device mark
of The Bible Reading Fellowship.

Published by
The Bible Reading Fellowship
15 The Chambers, Vineyard
Abingdon OX14 3FE, United Kingdom
Tel: +44 (0)1865 319700
Email: enquiries@brf.org.uk; Website: www.brf.org.uk
BRF is a Registered Charity

ISBN 978 0 85746 354 8
First edition 2015

Printed and bound in China